To Stefan,
May God's love and
light continue to fill
you abundantly

Endorsement

Dennis has a passion for the scientific discoveries that reveal truth in both the natural and supernatural realms of life. He does a really good job of breaking down the great divide between God and Science. Most people of faith are afraid to look to science for answers, and most people of science tend not to look to God for resolving any of the questions that science may bring up. This creates an "us and them" mentality, and Dennis has tackled both sides, removing that way of thinking altogether. Dennis invites us to see the facts that science presents and explore how these truths are confirmed in the Bible and in life all around us. If you are a person of faith, I hope you can get into this book with confidence that all things point to God, the giver of all life; who created things in such a way to reveal mystery and point to truth. If you are a person of science, I hope you are willing to consider God as possibly being the answer to questions science is bringing up. We don't need to choose sides but rather let's dive in and explore truth together the way Dennis is showing us in this powerful book.

Pastor, Jonathan Hanson
Abundant Life Church
Bellingham, Washington

I dedicate this book to
my son Tyler and
his lovely bride Lauren,
my daughter Hanna,
my future grandchildren,
their children,
their children's children,
and all who come after them.

A Quantum Case For God

by

Dennis Zetting

Published by

Quantum Creation Ministries

www.quantumcreation.net

Lynden, Washington USA

For permission requests, email info@quantumcreationministries.com, attention: Permission Coordinator.

Printed in the United States of America

Published by Quantum Creation Ministries, Lynden Washington

Unless otherwise stated all biblical quotations are taken from the New American Standard Bible, Copyright© 1995 by The Lockman Foundation, La Habra, California. Biblical lexicon references are taken from www.blueletterbible.org.

Book Cover Art & Design by Amani Hanson, Becoming Studios
Illustrations by Amrit Tigga
Editing: Jim Bryson (JamesLBryson@gmail.com)
Proofing: Emily-Anne Zornes (Em.Zornes@yahoo.com)
Typesetting, Design & Prepress: Jacque Peterson
(jacque@macaddicts.net)

Library of Congress Cataloging-in-Publication data
Zetting, Dennis.
A Quantum Case for God / Dennis Zetting
ISBN 978-0-9976819-0-1 (paperback)
Quantum physics. 2. String physics. 3. God. I. Title.

First Edition ~ 2016

Acknowledgements

This is my first book, and for those who have not written a book based on scientific facts, the amount of work it takes to complete the task is daunting. You learn quickly that it takes a village to write a book. I'm extremely grateful for my village.

As with every journey it begins with a first step. Thank you Harold Eberle for looking me straight in the eye and telling me that I must write this book. You gave me the inspiration to say *yes* to God and commit to writing on such a needed topic.

A special thank you goes to Jim Bryson for doing such a fabulous job editing and helping me to become a better writer. Faced with the task of simplifying the extremely complex world of quantum and string physics, you were invaluable at helping me have things make sense, maintain a consistent flow and incorporate a bit of lightheartedness.

Thank you to my physics associate-professor friend Mike Greiner for our discussions on these topics and taking the time out of his busy schedule to check my facts for accuracy.

Thank you Amani Hanson for the gorgeous book cover design, Emilyanne Zornes for your proofreading skills and Jacque Peterson for the detailed work of typesetting and prepress. Without your assistance, this book would look like a six year old's figure painting. Instead it came out looking like a masterpiece of art.

Thank you to the Quantum Creation team Jacque & Scott Peterson, Daniel & Joan (Joy) Statema, and Candice Eberle for your assistance and support in getting this message out to more people. We are ready to take another step forward.

A special thank you to my two biggest fans in this endeavor. First, to my incredible wife Randi. I'm blessed to have a wife who cares to hear and know what I teach and be actively involved. And to my amazing daughter Hanna, who is my number one student, giving me the encouragement to communicate this important message to the younger generation.

Contents

Endorsement

Dedication

Acknowledgements

Foreword iii

Introduction v

Chapter 1   Quantum and String Physics? 1

Chapter 2   The Big Bang 13

Chapter 3   Quantum Electrodynamics and Omnipresence 21

Chapter 4   Quantum Discovers New Realms of Reality 33

Chapter 5   Delayed Choice Quantum Eraser Effect - Omniscience 51

Chapter 6   Vibrations 63

Chapter 7   Additional Dimensions 87

Chapter 8   Time 115

Chapter 9   Making Sense of it All 143

Index 168

Bibliography 171

"Sometimes people ask if religion and science
are not opposed to one another.
They are: in the same sense that the thumb
and fingers are opposed to one another.
It is an opposition by means of which
anything can be grasped."

Sir William Henry Bragg,
Winner of the Nobel Prize in physics,
1915

Foreword

When I first met Dennis, he told me of his upcoming book involving Quantum physics, String theory and God. This immediately grabbed my attention. Trained as both a wildlife biologist and a Christian theologian, I had often marveled at the symmetry between science and the Bible. But at other times, the chasms between these fields of study, and the conflicts among the adherents of each, troubled me greatly. After all, if God is the author of both the natural world and the spiritual world, shouldn't the academic study of the natural agree with the testament of the spiritual? The division is further exacerbated as each side seeks to enhance their position by discrediting the other. Certain theologians, intent on a strict interpretation of Genesis, for example, reject the scientific findings that Earth is billions of years old. On the other hand, some scientists mock the loose or nonexistent standards of proof for core theological beliefs. It is a battle that has raged for centuries and claimed casualties on both sides. Believing scientists are held with suspicion by their colleagues. Scientifically-minded Christians are considered less-than faithful. And the questioning public views the entire debate with growing confusion and askance.

Enter Dennis Zetting, who has the mind of a physicist and the heart of a worshiper. Not content to alternate between each world depending on whose he is addressing, he has pursued the true unity of faith spoken of in Ephesians 4:13. Where many have attempted to join the dispirit sides of this age-old debate through compromise, essentially watering down the more contentious positions of each side, Dennis has taken a more credible and fruitful approach. Following his life-long passion, he has delved into the mind of science, embracing the wonders of discovery without fear of negative theological ramifications. Indeed, if God is the Creator of the universe, then he is the God of science. Remarkably, rather than limiting his theology, Dennis' exhaustive pursuit of modern physics has revealed the truth of God's word as recorded in the Bible. Genesis has found new relevance to the scientifically minded. And theologians are finding they no longer need to eschew science at a means of preserving their beliefs. It's as though each side has been saying the same thing all along. And, of course, they have! *The heavens declare the glory of God; the skies proclaim the work of his hands* (Psalms 19:1).

I encourage you to follow Dennis as he takes you on a journey through the mind of God as revealed by the world of modern physics. But don't expect to come away knowing all the answers. If science teaches us anything, it is that discovery only introduces us to greater and greater questions. As we learn more, the answers we originally sought become less relevant in the pursuit of greater vistas opening before us.

Finally, do not think you need to be either a physicist or a theologian to appreciate Dennis' work. In fact, he presents it especially for those who are neither. His gift of teaching makes complex quantum theories simple to grasp, and his open-minded approach to Christianity is never dogmatic or preachy. Dennis presents facts, ideas, theories and most importantly... wonderment. Let your imagination soar as you begin to realize things you've never seen before.

It's a new world waiting, an ancient guide revealing, the ascent of man fulfilling the call to go forth into all of creation...ALL of creation...and look, touch, reveal, learn and grow.

Dr. Harold R. Eberle
Worldcast Ministries
Yakima, Washington U.S.A.

Introduction

A Quantum Case for God

Like most in the Western world, I am fundamentally influenced by science. And for good reason. Since the Renaissance, science has become the bedrock of truth for our secularized, logical minds—a powerful voice, respected and revered, especially pertaining to our personal problems. If we are too fat, too old, too scared, or too lost, we trust some form of science for answers. Scientific diets, anti-aging drugs, counselors, psychiatrists, GPS's, and interstellar explorers purveying a never-ending stream of brighter futures and more slender waistlines.

I also believe in God, Christ and the Holy Spirit. I have a personal relationship that goes beyond explanations from traditional science.

Amidst my own burgeoning scientific outlook, I often found myself confused between Christianity and science over the universe's creation. I did not know how to reconcile the big bang theory with Genesis, for example. I trusted the scientific data, but I also trusted the Bible. The disparities raged in my divided mind. How could the universe have begun 13.8 billion years ago when the Bible implies that God created it 6,000-10,000 years ago, and in a 6-day period? Further, how could I rationalize the existence of dinosaurs millions of years ago when there is no Biblical record? Finally— and more germane to my raging dilemma—how could I objectively debate creationism vs. evolution with intelligent friends and observers?

Keep in mind I didn't set out to resolve these issues so I could have a ministry. I wanted these answers for my own peace of mind. I reasoned that if God created the universe and everything in it—the Earth, stars, and planets—then He also created the laws of physics. This would include gravity, electromagnetism, entropy, and why cats have kittens. Further, if God created the laws of physics, they should align with the concept of intelligent design. Somehow, science had to be consistent with a creator God, so I set out to reconcile the two—a created being bridging the gap between his Creator and all of creation. There were humbler tasks on the docket I guess, but this was mine.

Early in my search I realized that science is neutral when it comes to a creator God. Science really doesn't care who is up there. Rather, it wants to reveal scientific truth regardless of the theological or metaphysical implications. To do so, science describes discovered truth two ways:

a) Repeatable experiments (empirical data)

b) Mathematics (the language of science).

Notice that neither of these methods sets out to prove or disprove God's existence; that is not the mission of science. However, there are a few individuals—articulate and well-learned—causing much controversy and confusion. By taking an aggressive position derived from science, they attempt to discredit the existence of God while exalting paradigms opposing him. As with all things human, it is this vocal minority that garners the most public attention. I wrote this book, not just for them, but for all who need the whole picture before deciding the issues for themselves.

A Door Opens

My journey to reconcile science and Christianity took off late one Christmas Eve as I struggled to assemble a ping-pong table for my son. To distract myself from the directions, which had been translated from Mandarin to English to Swahili, I had the TV playing in the background. About 2 in the morning, I found myself captivated by a NOVA program called The Elegant Universe, hosted by Brian Greene from Columbia University. Professor Greene shared what is occurring in our world from the perspective of quantum and string physics. I suddenly lost all interest in Ping and Pong. High School science never taught me the things that Professor Greene was presenting. Sure, I knew that Newton's apple fell, Einstein's theory soared, and Galileo's head was on the block, but nothing ever grabbed me like modern physics. It dawned on me that the most intelligent people on the planet, funded by billions of dollars, were devoted to revolutionary fields of science—notably quantum and string physics—of which I knew so little. Vast, uncharted realities appeared before me—beyond what I could see, touch, taste or hear. I knew instinctively that this knowledge held the key to my quest. Like my healing years before, that Christmas Eve shifted my life in a new direction, opening a world connecting science with God.

Today, I am passionate in my research of how science explains the universe. Before studying science, I used to read the Bible to enrich only my spiritual life. Now, I am amazed that it also addresses current findings in quantum and string physics.

What We Thought We Knew

Scientists are discovering incredible principles at the sub-atomic level, things such as quantum entanglement, quantum tunneling, additional dimensions and wave/particle duality. Like all great discoveries, these are baffling the scientific community and reversing traditional theories long held as indisputable truth. Science has opened a Pandora's box, revealing how little we actually know about the universe. In the late 1800's, science thought it knew everything. Oh, the bliss of ignorance! Then along came quantum physics and now science has more questions than answers, humbling the mightiest thinkers among us.

In truth, when it comes to the wacky, egalitarian world of modern physics, there are no experts. The true authorities are the first to say that they don't understand it. Professor Richard Feynman states, *"You see, my physics students don't understand it either. That is because I don't understand it. Nobody does." (QED the Strange Theory of Light and Matter,* Richard Feynman, Princeton University Press, Princeton, 2006 pg. 9.) And that is key to appreciating the revolution that modern physics has ignited. Conventional modes of inquiry, experimentation, proof and confidence no longer apply.

Please take this as a warning. As you endeavor to understand everything in this book, not only will your knowledge base grow, your paradigm of what constitutes truth *must change* to grasp the fullness of the modern scientific awakening. Imagine walking up to the vast Pacific Ocean and filling a meager 5-gallon bucket. That's what science knows about the universe—a miniscule fraction, yet the implications of that sliver is altering how we see the world around us. My task is to take these crazy phenomena and condense them within a single book, in language that the uninitiated can comprehend. And if I spark an insatiable thirst to know more, I will be ecstatic to welcome you to the club.

Atheism, Faith, and God

I am not here to prove that God exists. However, I will prove there is sufficient evidence from quantum and string physics that unequivocally removes the basis for saying that a creator *cannot* exist. From a scientific perspective, we can no more say that God cannot exist than we can say that the *many worlds interpretation*, or the *Copenhagen interpretation* (prominent hypotheses in modern physics) cannot exist.

When I sit one-on-one with people who don't believe in God and share the realities of the universe from a scientific perspective, they are amazed at the craziness of quantum phenomena. When I then connect the bizarre world of quantum and string physics with things written thousands of years ago in the Bible, a new openness to listen about a creator God occurs. While I enjoy my private discussions with atheists and agnostics, it is time to let more people in on the conversation.

Thank you for investing your time to consider this new scientific information. Our study is for everybody. I will rely on scientific information, not theology or religious doctrine, in presenting a quantum case that God is a viable reality. Although we'll use some biblical references, they are included purely to relate to laws of physics.

For hard-core atheists who say, "a creator God cannot exist," I will challenge your beliefs, and it will be your responsibility to back up your arguments against what science says. I invite you to come with your arguments.

For those who say, "I don't *believe* in God," you may be more of an agnostic than an atheist, one who doesn't know if there is a God, a god, or gods, but you decide to take a position on the matter. Many factors can shape this view: perhaps a creator God seems stupid, silly or impossible; perhaps you used to believe in God but something changed your mind; perhaps the concept of God seems fabricated by needy people. There are many reasons for taking the "I don't *believe* in God" stance. I respect your position. I think that everyone has this belief at some time in our lives.

The information presented here is designed to be scientifically neutral, allowing readers to form a broader view of the universe and determine if a creator God could exist. I hope to give you new insights by which to evaluate your position.

To readers who hold to Judeo-Christian beliefs I hope that you gain as many insights as I did and find the information a helpful way to dialogue with others. Incredibly, the God of the Bible aligns with every quantum and string phenomena discussed in this book.

Historically, it has been difficult to align science with God. This is because science was limited to three dimensions of natural reality: length, width and depth. In contrast, the Bible describes God in spiritual dimensions. So when science could not extend rules of proof to the spiritual realms, it simply dismissed the notion of spiritual realms as ridiculous. Today, with the discoveries in quantum and string physics, additional dimensions and realms are reality—necessity even—birthing remarkable scientific discoveries that support a creator God. Science is no longer the enemy of faith nor the expunger of God in our modern consciousness. Remarkably, science is quickly becoming an advocate of phenomenal power and unseen realities previously heralded only by ancient belief structures.

For those of all faiths, I invite you to test the laws of physics against your faith. Some will align with your faith and will be encouraging news. However, please don't play favorites by accepting certain principles while discarding those incongruent with your faith. If a faith only addresses one or two of these principles, then we must ask, "is there a reality greater than my faith?" Many faiths are built on truths; however, most faiths do not encompass all truth, including scientific truth. Our goal is to fully align truth with science.

I invite you to do further research on all the subjects presented. Most books, such as The Elegant Universe by Brian Greene, are difficult to understand for the novice reader. I suggest starting out learning from credible informative videos on YouTube, World Science University or Public TV.

Finally, do not be dismayed if the principles of physics introduced in this book are unfamiliar. The most daunting issue facing anyone learning a new science is the language. Science has its own language, as does engineering, firefighting, law, ministry, or the U. S. Navy. Ironically, foreign languages have a way of masking simple concepts with complex-sounding speech. Failure to overcome this barrier can keep us from rich discoveries in other realms of thought or culture. Here is a brief example:

Have you ever wanted to go visit a far-off country, but hesitated because you don't speak the language? Perhaps you wanted to visit Russia, but not a touristy area like St. Petersburgh where you might find some English-speakers. Instead, you want to go to Achinsk where the people only speak the mother tongue. You realize it would be a great idea to learn some basics of the Russian language, lest you order fillet of sole in a restaurant and they bring you a soiled shoe. Sadly, when you discover how difficult Russian is, you cancel your trip and never fulfill your dreams.

Quantum and string physics can present the same challenges. These are fascinating places to visit but the language barrier can be daunting. Tragically, those not fluent in science-speak avoid the countries of quantum or string altogether.

Realizing this issue, I have strived to simplify not only the scientific concepts but also the language through which they are conveyed. I hope my readers will want to visit often, stay a while, and enjoy their trips.

This book is about connecting people with science, and science with God. It is about learning a new language, new concepts, and answering age-old questions—often with new questions, but couched in insights never before imagined.

Let's get started!

Dennis Zetting, *Author*

Chapter 1

~~~~~~~~~~~~~~~~~~~~~~~~~~~~~~~~~~~~~~

What Are Quantum & String Physics?

One hundred years ago, it was common for people not to believe life exists on other planets. It was also common to assume life *cannot* exist on other planets—that it is impossible, even illogical, to consider such nonsense. However, times have changed.

Today, cosmologists estimate the universe contains billions, perhaps a trillion, galaxies, each consisting of hundreds of billions of stars and planets. Conservative tallies estimate 100 sextillion (100,000,000,000,000,000,00 0,000,000) stars in the universe (that's a big number), many with attendant planets and moons. Adding to the growing recognition that the universe is a vast and uncharted place, cosmologists are finding more and more planets that could sustain life—as we understand life. To date, scientists estimate millions of planets exist that are hospitable to carbon-based organisms.

Based on these findings, the possibility of life on other planets is realistic. Sure, there are those who still don't believe that life exists on other planets. We should respect their opinion. They have adapted a wait-and-see position: *wait* until science goes to another planet and *see* the life-form they bring back.

Please note a subtle difference in positions, however. Most skeptics are not saying that life *cannot* exist on other planets. Instead, they are saying that they are *not convinced* that life exists on other planets. This is a powerful distinction. As more and more data comes in, it is becoming rare for a person to retain the staunch position that life *cannot* exist outside of Earth.

Such a restrictive assertion seems foolish today, although it is similar to the position held by modern atheists—absolute certainty of the non-existence of God despite mounting evidence to the contrary. Just as the arguments over cosmic life from the last century are yielding to present scientific discoveries, so also, modern physics is eroding the staunch atheistic position that God *cannot* exist. The new information flowing from quantum and string physics, which we will discuss in detail, makes the outdated arguments of atheism null and void.

Origins of Atheism

Although the roots of atheism date back to ancient Greek philosophers Socrates, Anaxagoras, and Protagoras (among others), outright atheistic belief exploded during the Enlightenment Period of the late 18th century. Ever since Sir Isaac Newton's famous encounter with a Macintosh revealed the gravity of his situation, people have been obsessed with how the universe works.

In Newton's time, scientific endeavors operated with the framework of the four dimensions of the physical world: height, width, depth and spatial time, while being limited to the natural forces of gravity and electromagnetism. Working within these criteria encompasses what is known as classical physics or Newtonian science (in recognition of the venerable Sir Isaac).

Physics is the study of matter and its motion through time and space. Apples had been falling from trees well before Newton's day. However, no one knew why they fell. By studying large objects like planets, Newton was able to create a mathematical formula called *the inverse-square law of gravitation* and establish a foundational understanding of gravity. Newton wrote:

> *"Every particle of matter in the universe attracts every other particle with a force that is directly proportional to the product of the masses of the particles and inversely proportional to the square of the distance between them."*
>
> *Philosophiæ Naturalis Principia Mathematica*
> *(translated from Latin), Newton, Benjamin Motte*
> *publisher, 1687 Original language: Latin*

Newton's standard mathematical formula for gravitation was an astounding discovery. Einstein eventually came along and improved upon Newton's formula by introducing the theories of special relativity and general relativity, and with these, one the most popular mathematical equations in history: $E = mc^2$.

Classical physics is honored for the creation of the standard scientific method of testing. The scientific method says that for something to be "true" it must be observed, measured, and proven to show cause and effect.

To see the impact of the scientific method, let's take cancer research as an example. Company X believes they have a new way to treat a form of cancer. For their hypothesis to be proven true by the classical scientific method, the subject must be observed. This can be done through various means: visual, microscope, ultrasound, MRI, etc. In addition, the hypothesis needs to be measured through controlled experiments, which include specific ways to predict a particular cause and effect. In cancer research, this involves measuring the changes occurring between treated cancer cells and non-treated cancer cells. The last hurdle is to prove a consistent cause and effect. The results from the measured experiments must have the same outcomes every time they are performed.

From these disciplines of testing and proof, philosophies arose, relying on the same rigors as scientific discovery to determine truth. This is the environment in which atheism flourished.

Modern Age

Now, to be clear, the requirements arising from the scientific method of inquiry have built our modern age. After all, it is comforting to know that the 20-story building that our loved one works in will not collapse in gale-force winds. This confidence is rooted in the standard testing regime of observe, measure, prove cause and effect.

The scientific method tells us that when properly assembled, steel is an excellent material for framing skyscrapers, whereas cardboard is a poor material. Of course, we could also arrive at this conclusion because steel builders are thriving today, while cardboard builders went out of business after the first rainstorm! But scientifically, the observe-measure-cause/

effect process has proven the usefulness of one material over the other, and we are the beneficiaries.

Certainly, our modern age is rife with examples of epic failures. However, it is telling that when things do go wrong, we turn to the same scientific method to uncover and remedy the failings of the science behind the flawed design. In the end, we rely on science once again for our wellbeing.

When the Twin Towers were attacked, set aflame and collapsed, scientific observation told us that the fireproof cladding, which had not been properly applied to the buildings' steel frames during construction, must be applied correctly in all future buildings. When the walkways of the Hyatt Regency Hotel in Kansas City collapsed, analysis through the scientific method showed that the supporting structures had been overloaded by a factor of four. The faulty calculation was revised and the walkways rebuilt. The toll from both of these catastrophes was horrific, but the resulting changes illustrate our continued reliance on the scientific method to advance from failure.

Societies throughout the world depend on the truths derived from the scientific method and apply them to all walks of life. People want safety, convenience and advancement; the scientific method provides this within acceptable degrees of certainty. So far, so good.

The problem with the scientific method, however, is that it focuses on things that have a lot of mass and exist within the four dimensions of the natural world—width, height, depth and spacetime—leading people to define "reality" as that which they see, touch, hear, taste and smell on a daily basis. This restriction is a boon for atheists and a handicap for modern physicists, as we will see.

Atheistic Quicksand

For centuries, atheists and creationists were at a philosophical stalemate. Atheists put the onus on creationists to prove God through the scientific method, something that creationists could not do to the satisfaction of atheists. Since creationists could not observe God, measure God with controlled experiments, and thereby prove God, there was no God to the atheists. Creationists, on the other hand, countered that atheists could not prove scientifically there was *no* God. However, atheism possessed the high ground, requiring scientific standards to prove truth. Their position, therefore, was one of logic. They claimed that since there is no scientific evidence of a creator God—only stories and myths—a creator God is an illogical and absurd idea, unworthy to be considered even as a possibility.

Note the genius of their position. By requiring creationists to prove a creator under the restrictive scientific method, atheists inhabited a seemingly unassailable position. For centuries, they deluged culture from their lofty perches with countless examples of how science proves that truth lies only within the classical scientific method.

Unfortunately for atheists, their bastion of strength has proven to be their undoing. By stating that there is NO possibility for God to exist, they have entrenched themselves in an all-or-nothing position.

Modern quantum science has proven them wrong.

There's a New Sheriff in Town

For this discussion to make any sense, we need to know some of the differences between classical (Newtonian) science, quantum science and string science. Now, if these are unfamiliar terms to you, don't panic! I'll make it easy to understand, right up to the point where you say, *"Wow! There's a lot more going on in the universe than I thought."*

You are not alone. Although the bizarre world of quantum and strings has revolutionized science, most of the world has never heard of these fields and has little knowledge of their ramifications. No problem; this is why we are having this discussion. The offshoot of modern physics is that classical physics is no longer the big dog. Quantum and string physics is where it's at. As we understand that there are more realities occurring than what we see in four-dimensional realities, we will see life differently, forcing us to re-evaluate our belief in many areas, including the existence of a creator God.

Pop Quantum Physics

Despite the unfamiliarity with quantum physics, "quantum" is a popular buzzword in today's culture. Every time I mention I study quantum physics, people light up with curiosity. This is good. We need to learn about this chaotic phenomena because the quantum world has uncovered never-before-known mysteries of how the universe works.

To put quantum physics in perspective, let's first take a look at space.

Through television shows such as <u>Cosmos: A Spacetime Odyssey,</u> (hosted by astrophysicist Neil DeGrasse Tyson), and space photos from NASA, cosmology (the study of the universe) is getting a lot of interest. People are fascinated by stars, planets, and the potential they hold. And for good reason—there are so many of them! Cosmologists estimate conservatively that there exist 10^{23} stars in the universe. That's 100,000,000,000,000,000,000,000 stars. Wow! This number is so large, the average person has no way of grasping how big it is. Maybe this will help. It is estimated there are 7.5×10^{18} grains of sand on Earth. That's 7,500,000,000,000,000,000—a huge number, certainly. But if you subtracted the grains of sand from the stars in the universe, there would still be 99,992,500,000,000,000,000,000 stars left over. The enormous number of grains of sand barely puts a dent in the fantastically huge number of stars.

Now, let's compare the stars in the universe with the tiny world of atoms and particles. (Particles are the sub-atomic parts comprising atoms.) The particles in one drop of water equal the number of stars in the universe. Considering that the particles of atoms make up everything in the universe, not just a drop of water, the vast, sub-atomic world is almost beyond comprehension.

Get Down With Quantum

Quantum Science is the study of energy, matter and motion at the sub-atomic (or nanoscopic) scale. Its job is not only to count all those particles, but to understand *what* they do, *why* they do it and what *makes* them do it. Science thought for centuries that the atom was the smallest thing in existence; then it discovered that atoms consist of even smaller components called *particles*. Quantum science explores these particle components of atoms: quarks, electrons, muons, taus and neutrinos. *Quantum* is derived from the Latin word *quanta,* which means "a discrete amount" and refers to the discovery that some physical quantities can only change in whole amounts.

Let's use the following illustrations to step down to the quantum level. (See diagram 1.1) Picture a baby; she has cells, including blood cells. These blood cells are comprised of molecules. Molecules are made up of bonded atoms. Atoms are made of particles such as, up quarks, down quarks and electrons. It is here at the sub-atomic stage that the crazy world of quantum happens. Particles are believed to be comprised of tiny vibrating strands of energy called strings.

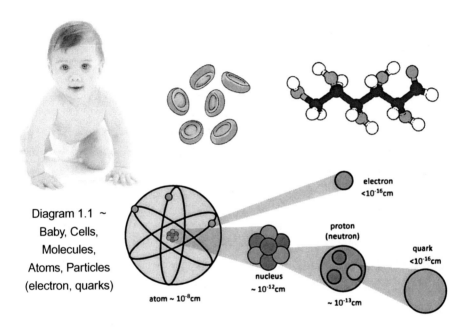

Diagram 1.1 ~
Baby, Cells,
Molecules,
Atoms, Particles
(electron, quarks)

electron
$<10^{-16}$cm

proton
(neutron)

quark
$<10^{-16}$cm

nucleus
$\sim 10^{-12}$cm

atom $\sim 10^{-8}$cm

$\sim 10^{-13}$cm

2-2-2, 4-4-4, Pit

Atoms are the building blocks of the universe. There are currently 118 known atoms, also known as elements. Hydrogen, carbon and oxygen are well known atoms, while terbium, hassium and bismuth haven't quite hit the popularity bandwagon. Everything in the universe that you can see and touch, including you, your house, the stars and the burrito you had for dinner, are made up of combinations of these atoms. The primary difference between atoms is the number of protons and electrons each has.

Getting down to the infinitesimal components of atoms has uncovered how atoms interact with other atoms, and how they exchange energy. At the nucleus of atoms lie protons and neutrons, which are comprised of even smaller particles called *quarks*. These particles are bonded together by gluon particles, which are an incredibly powerful force called *the strong nuclear force.* Nuclear power plants and nuclear bombs are based on this energy within atoms.

The tiny particles revolving around the nucleus are called *electrons.* They are extremely busy characters with two primary jobs. Their first job is to fill their orbital shells. An orbital shell is the range of distance from the nucleus that an electron inhabits as it orbits; each shell has a particular number of electrons required to fill it. It is like a universal game of Pit.

Have you ever played Pit? You are in a frenzied game of trying to collect a complete category of 8 cards by trading out non-matching cards and looking to collect matching cards. Electrons do the same thing. Most atoms have incomplete shells and are either trying to loan out their unneeded electrons, or borrow needed electrons from another atom. When an atom with its electrons finds another atom(s) that collectively fills both their shell levels, the atoms are allowed to bond with each other. For example, a sodium (Na) atom will bond with a chlorine (Cl) atom because collectively the total of their electrons fills their shell requirements. Sodium chloride (NaCl) is formed, known by its everyday name as table salt. Ding....ding... Pit!

The first step for atoms to bond together is to find other atoms with appropriate electron combinations. The other primary job of the electron is to obtain or release electromagnetic energy depending on the needs at any given moment. This electromagnetic energy is what actually bonds atoms together. It's like a universal game of hot-potato. An electron collects a packet of electromagnetic energy and it's a hot-potato, because the electron can't keep it for long. It has to release the energy and look to collect another hot-potato. Electrons never really gather up a resource of energy. They constantly need energy, but they can't store it for a rainy day. It's a crazy cycle of needing to borrow energy and then give it back.

Electrons get this electromagnetic energy by interacting with light particles called *photons.* The scientific name for this is *quantum electrodynamics.* We will discuss this in greater depth in upcoming chapters.

Little Big Man

A marked difference between quantum physics and classical physics is how each deals with things like molecules, cells and 100-story skyscrapers. Classical physics lends itself well to observable predictions of relatively large things (above the atomic level). But when we look at extremely tiny things such as a single electron of an atom, predictable cause and effect measurement goes out the window because we can't say for sure where the electron is at any given time. This is when we need quantum physics.

For example, consider 70,000 people at a Seattle Seahawks football game. If the Seahawks score, it is predictable that the large Seattle crowd will cheer. This is an observable prediction made by classical physics. But if we took a single fan (we'll name him Les) out of the group, the predictability that Les would cheer for the Seahawks is reduced to the *possibility* that he would cheer at all. This is a measurement that quantum physics would make.

At the individual level, a number of factors affect the possibility that Les would cheer the moment the Seahawks score:

- He could be buying a hotdog.

- He could be texting.

- He could be in the men's room.

- He could be a Broncos fan.

- He could have just lost 100 dollars on his fantasy league.

Now, if you think of the 70,000 fans as all the particles making up, say, a living cell, then an individual person at the game is a single particle of that cell. Hopefully you see that the entire cell is much easier to observe, measure and predict, just as the actions of the 70,000 fans are predictable. Predicting Les's reaction, however, requires probability based on possibilities.

Classical science likes to explain the world from the stadium perspective. Quantum, on the other hand, explains the world from the perspective of Les standing in line for a hotdog. (What are the odds it will be the dark mustard vs. the yellow?)

Strings: The Final Frontier

Now, before things get too rosy, we must acknowledge that the world of quantum physics has a problem—it doesn't work well with gravity. In fact, physics says that gravity and quantum physics should not be able to exist together. But since science can prove that both gravity and quantum physics exist, there must be a means for both to exist—something we don't understand yet. Einstein spent his final years looking for the answer, which he called *the unification theory,* something to tie all four forces of nature: electromagnetism, strong nuclear, weak nuclear AND gravity, together into one unified theory. Sadly, Einstein passed away before he found the means to string all these forces together. It was not until the mid-1970's that physicists discovered the answer that eluded the father of relativity. (But, this was also around the same time that disco music was sweeping the nation, so nobody cared.)

String physics, also known as unification theory, M-theory, or superstring theory, (we will use the most popular moniker: string theory), differs from quantum physics by taking into account all four forces of nature: electromagnetism, strong nuclear, weak nuclear and gravity. String theory postulates that particles of atoms are actually made up of tiny vibrating strings of energy all vibrating at different frequencies like guitar strings. Further, the vibration frequency of each string determines what kind of particle it is: a quark, a gluon, an electron or another. According to string theory, the universe is one gigantic symphony just stayin' alive.

Horton Hears a String

As inclusive as string theory is, it still has some hurdles to overcome. For starters, these tiny vibrating strands of energy are so tiny that scientists can't observe them. It's like Horton the elephant in the Dr. Seuss story *Horton Hears a Who.* For most of the story Horton, with his incredible hearing, is the only one able to hear the tiny beings in Whoville. Likewise, string physicists can "see" strings mathematically because they can prove these vibrating strings exist, but they can't produce a single one for us to hear or see. String theorists long for the day when they will be able to show the world the realities of strings just as the jungle animals eventually heard the Whos.

To see how fundamental string theory is, keep in mind that these vibrating strings make up particles, which make up atoms, which make up molecules, which make up all the matter in the universe. Therefore, string theory, as we understand physics at present, is the foundation of all we know in the universe. More amazing is that these strings of energy are so small, if you enlarged a single atom to the size of the universe, one string in that atom would only be the size of a tree. That's pretty tiny!

Sadly, the public's ignorance of these startling discoveries is profound. Quantum science has been around for over 100 years, and yet the average person knows little of it. String physics has been around for a mere 40 years, and most people have never heard of it. But everybody knows that Elvis is dead, the moon has footprints and The Matrix was the best movie ever! And yet, from these unknown branches of revolutionary science, the most influential discoveries in every major field of science in the next century will arise. Advances in biology, technology, psychology, history, chemistry, health and yes…entertainment, will be a direct result of quantum and string physics.

Blind Leading Blind

To the layman, science's advances might seem much ado about nothing. This is because most people still draw their conclusions from the classical physics viewpoint. If they can taste it, see it, hear it and carry it off in the truck, then they conclude it exists. Such a viewpoint differs greatly from the path that modern scientists must take. Their eyes are math, their intuition is probability and their conclusions lead to greater discoveries—and also to greater questions. Here's what reality is like for a modern scientist.

Imagine that you grew up blind but enjoy hiking forest paths. On your walks, you could still perceive many things in your immediate surroundings: fresh air on your face, humidity in your breath, the aroma of flowers, and the smell of smoke from a nearby campers' morning fire. Certainly, you could hear many things as well: your own voice, birds chirping, water lapping against stones. Touch would tell you of rough bark, smooth leaves and the warm palm of a companion. From all these sensory inputs, you would know there is more around you. However, you wouldn't know exactly what it is. Blind and restricted to the path, you wouldn't know the extent of the plants, flowers, animals and dirt that you sense. Neither would you know of mountains, rivers, stars, planets, or the universe. Yet, even limited by blindness, you would know that realities exist beyond blindness because you have evidence of things you don't fully understand.

That is where modern science has taken us so far. We know the realities of what we can detect. Yet we know there is much more going on beyond our immediate senses. Therefore, we are impelled to continue walking.

Chapter 2

The Big Bang

The year was 1927, and much of the Western world was experiencing the prosperity of the Roaring 20's. People were unaware of the immense shift from abundance to poverty that was about to occur. The stock market crash of 1929 would launch much of the world into the depths of the Great Depression, radically changing modern life forever. But another shift was also about to take place. In 1927, Monsignor Georges Lemaitre, a Roman Catholic priest and cosmologist, challenged the entrenched philosophy of Plato and Aristotle that the heavens—the sun, moon and stars—had always existed just as they were, and that they would continue thus. Plato and Aristotle's eternal steady-state universe had been the reigning philosophy for the past 2,200 years. Contrary to this thought, Lemaitre did not believe that galaxies were fixed in one place, but were moving away from each other. Rapidly.

This type of forward thinking was not accepted within the cosmology community at the time, as nearly every major cosmologist believed in the eternal steady-state universe philosophy. Further, the fact that this new thinking came from a priest threatened the scientific community that feared mysticism was going to be brought into the equation. However, in 1929, Edwin Hubble concluded that the galaxies were, in fact, drifting apart, giving scientific evidence for Lemaitre's theory.

Hubble was able to confirm the theory of expansion by measuring the redshift of distant galaxies. Redshift occurs when light waves emitted from an object, such as a star or a galaxy, are measured and found to be moving towards the red end of the light spectrum. This scientifically proves that the object(s) are moving away from the observer. Blueshift, on the other hand, occurs when light waves emitted from an object move toward the blue end of the spectrum. This means the object is moving towards the observer. (We will study the light spectrum in detail in later chapters.) In every galaxy Hubble measured, he discovered a redshift. The results were astounding. Lemaitre was correct. The entire universe was expanding.

By 1931, buoyed by the confirmation of his far-out ideas, Lemaitre expanded his cosmological theory to propose that the universe had a beginning. According to Lemaitre, if galaxies were moving away from each other, then we could assume that galaxies must have been closer together at one time. Lemaitre's conclusion was that all galaxies must have started at one point in space, a "primeval atom." And with this radical idea, the shift was on. Plato and Aristotle's philosophy, that the universe had always existed, was dealt a lethal blow. It was the genesis of the big bang theory.

The big bang didn't get its name until 18 years later, in 1949. It was accidentally coined during a BBC radio program when Fred Hoyle called Lemaitre's theory a "Big Bang idea." Although Hoyle was in opposition to Lemaitre's theory and meant for the comment to be derogatory, it captured the essence of Lemaitre's ideas, and the name stuck. As it turns out, according to our present understanding, the beginning of the universe didn't have a "big bang," but the term found a place in popular culture's lexicon. In 1993, Sky & Telescope Magazine sponsored a contest to change the name to something more accurate. After receiving over 13,000 entries, the judges didn't find one name worthy of a change, and so one of the most recognized theories in all of science ended up with one of the most inaccurate names in history.

The development of the big bang theory has come a long way since Hubble's discoveries in 1929. Billions and billions of dollars have been invested in the study of the cosmos. And billions more have been spent building atom smashers where scientists collide sub-atomic particles together and examine what happens. (Remember breaking your toys to figure out what was inside them? Yeah, same thing.)

After all the scientific discovery, here is what we know so far about the development of the universe. *(Taken from The Big Bang, a documentary video by Lawrence Krauss and Michio Kaku, 2015).*

Pre-time, prior to the big bang, there is nothing. No energy, no matter, no time and no space. It is the beginning of the universe.

- At 0 seconds a *singularity* occurs, containing all the energy and matter in the universe. It is condensed into a space smaller than the size of a sub-atomic particle. It is 10 trillion trillion times hotter than the core of our sun. The four forces of nature—gravity, strong nuclear, weak nuclear and electromagnetism—are combined into one super force. The singularity that is the universe starts expanding.

- At 10^{-36} Planck seconds (.00000000000000000000000000000000 00001 of a second) after the initial singularity occurs, the four forces begin to separate. The first to separate is gravity, followed by the strong and weak nuclear forces, then electromagnetism. *(note: there are 1,000,000,000,000,000,000,000,000,000,000,0 00,000,000,000 Planck seconds in 1 regular second, (so saying 10^{-36} Planck Seconds is a really, really, really short time!)*

- At 10^{-32} Planck seconds, the universe has expanded to the size of a baseball. (No telling if the Mets are in the playoffs yet.) It is pure energy and radiation. There is no matter and no atoms at this time.

- At 10^{-6} Planck seconds (not even 1 full second has elapsed since the emergence of the singularity), the universe is in a liquid, soup-like, state about the size of our solar system, filled with energy turning into matter—the particle building blocks of atoms. Now the greatest battle in the history of the universe takes place. For every particle of matter, there exists a particle of anti-matter. But matter and anti-matter can't exist together. They seek each other out, and when they come in contact, they annihilate each other. Within 1 millionth of a second, the mêlée is over and somehow matter wins. According to physicists, all matter should have been destroyed by anti-matter. But the universe ends up filled with matter. Of course, if that hadn't happened, I wouldn't be writing this book and you wouldn't be reading it, because we wouldn't exist. We are the leftovers of the matter/anti-matter battle. History is written by the survivors. That's all that matters.

- At 1 second after the singularity, the universe has grown to 1,000 times our solar system. It is flooded with sub-atomic particles called *quarks*. The universe has cooled down enough for the quarks to start bonding together to form protons and neutrons.

- At 3 minutes, the protons and neutrons begin to bond into the nuclei of atoms.

- At 300,000 years, electrons join with protons and neutrons to form atoms. (Think of atoms as the universal late-bloomers.)

- At 200 million years, the first stars are formed.

- At 1 billion years, galaxies are formed.

- At 9 billion years, Earth is established (roughly 4.5 billion years ago).

- At 13.8 billion years, approximately 45 minutes after a wild New Year's Eve party, you are formed.

- At 13.8 billion years, you are wondering when the next season of House of Cards will come out.

These discoveries have forever changed our understanding of the universe. Lemaitre caused a huge paradigm shift in scientific thinking. Plato and Aristotle saw the natural world here on Earth as changing and imperfect, while envisioning the distant world of the cosmos as unchanging and perfect. But we now know better.

Biblical Turnoff

Lemaitre's theory marked a victory for the church as well as science because science could now support the belief that the universe had a beginning, such as what is written in Genesis. *In the beginning, God created the heavens and the earth* (Genesis 1:1). And, *In the beginning was the Word, and the Word was with God, and the Word was God* (John 1: 1). Both scriptures pointed to a beginning.

However, this theological victory ran into problems. Although there was now a beginning, atheists, evolutionists and naturalists found the Genesis story to be inconsistent with the actual development of Earth, as understood by science.

Genesis gives an order of creation as follows:

1. Heavens & Earth (universe)
2. Light
3. Heavens
4. Plants
5. Stars
6. Water creatures and birds
7. Land creatures
8. Humans

In contrast, science presents a different order:

1. Super-force of energy
2. Gravity, strong & weak nuclear forces, light
3. Stars
4. Galaxies
5. Sun
6. Earth
7. Water
8. Water creatures
9. Land animals
10. Land plants
11. Birds
12. Humans.

Adding to the incongruity of the two orders was the question: how could the creation story in Genesis, which was described as occurring in six days, compete with the 13.8 billion years of necessary development uncovered by science? Parties opposing creationism believed that a book inspired by God should at least be consistent with the order and dating discovered by science. Indeed, this continues today to be a topic of discussion in debates involving creationists, atheists, evolutionists and naturalists.

The apparent disconnect between Genesis and science is a powerful argument for those who oppose the concept of God. Since the biblical accounts of Genesis, Chapters 1 and 2, are not consistent with science, the concept of God has lost favor in the minds of millions of people. This has even led some churches to alter their doctrines to propose that Genesis is a metaphor of creation, not an actual account of creation process.

The Bible Gets Help from Quantum & String Physics

Billions of dollars and countless hours have produced astounding details of the universe. However, science doesn't know what existed before the big bang, nor what caused the big bang, or even the source of the energy produced by the big bang.

Still, quantum and string physics has become extremely relevant to discussions about the universe and God, to the point where any theories must include these branches of modern physics. This is important because most people think about the big bang solely from a classical physics perspective without realizing its limitations. Trying to discuss the universe without incorporating quantum and string theory is akin to discussing how to reach the moon without including advanced math such as algebra, calculus and geometry, and only using basic math of addition, subtraction, multiplication and division. You might get to Cape Canaveral but you could never get to the Sea of Tranquility.

One wouldn't say they were an expert in the field of mathematics if they had a good understanding of the basic four—add, subtract, multiply and divide—but knew nothing of algebra or calculus. This is where 99% of people stand regarding the big bang. It is as though they have based their beliefs from a perspective of basic math alone. It is one thing to base a belief from a limited perspective; it is an entirely different thing to launch accusations against issues such as the topic of God from that same perspective. The universe is complex. It is no longer feasible to pose opinions concerning the universe without some basic understanding of quantum and string physics, especially when these opinions include the impossibility of God.

The upcoming chapters on quantum and string physics will yield a fresh perspective of the Genesis creation story. Purported inconsistencies between the big bang theory and the Bible's creation story have changed with an adequate knowledge of modern physics. Where Biblical scholars have interpreted the Bible as full of anthropomorphisms about an emotionless God, and atheists have viewed the Bible as silliness and conjecture, we will see that quantum and string physics support a more literal interpretation. In the end, we will discover there is no discrepancy between the origin of the universe and the Genesis creation story.

Chapter 3

Quantum Electrodynamics & Omnipresence

Light is one of the most fascinating and baffling phenomenon in the universe—to the point where scientists have yet to adequately define it. They are actively investigating the breadth of this strange substance, but for our purposes, we only need to be enlightened on the basics of light. Though by basic, I mean we will need to understand a specific branch of quantum physics.

Remember, from Chapter 1, the electrons which play hot-potato with energy and are in constant need of more? They get that energy from light. Scientists call it electromagnetic energy. Basically, light is a force of nature that combines electricity (think lightning) and magnetism. The part of quantum physics governing how light feeds the needs of the insatiable electrons is called *quantum electrodynamics.*

Light Speed

Everyone knows light is fast. According to Einstein, nothing in the universe can travel faster than light. Light traveling in a vacuum zips along at 186,281 miles per second (300,000,000 kilometers per second). That's 671 million miles per hour. In a year, light would travel roughly 6 trillion miles. This is what is known as a *light-year.* (It is also the time it takes a fruitcake to decay to half its life.)

Getting down to the quantum stage, a single particle of light is called a *photon.* Now, don't confuse it with the proton of an atom. Photons are not a part of an atom. They are individual packets of energy, and are found everywhere in the universe.

David Blatner, in his book Spectrums, describes photons:

> *"Photons – known as the carrier particles of electromagnetism – are literally what make our universe possible. Light – the oscillation of electromagnetic waves, the transmission of photons – is like the lifeblood of the cosmos, carrying packets of energy from one atom to another...."*
>
> Spectrums: Our Mind Boggling Universe from Infinitesimal to Infinity, Blatner, David. Bloomsbury, New York. 2014

Notice that Dr. Blatner mentions both waves and packets. This is because light has a dual personality. Light has the ability to be both a particle (photon) and a wave (wave). Quantum physicists call this phenomenon *superposition*. When light engages with something like an electron, it is a photon. When light is not engaging with something, it is usually acting as a wave. Light waves act like ocean waves, except these waves are oscillating up and down through space.

You are Only Coming Through in Waves

To understand the properties of light waves, we need to understand wavelength and frequency.

Let's start at a pond. Tossing a stone into the water causes ripples. These ripples are similar to light waves traveling throughout the universe. Now, if we instead tossed a large rock into the pond, the ripples would be larger. If we were astute (and motivated) we could measure the wave height and its speed, determining how long it takes for a complete wave (ripple up and ripple down) to pass a fixed point.

Scientists measure light waves based on the same properties. They determine wavelength by measuring the length of a wave from beginning to end. They determine frequency by measuring how frequently the wave goes up and down (oscillates) in one second. Frequency is measured in units of hertz (Hz). So a frequency of 1 Hz means that 1 complete wave occurs in 1 second. The higher the frequency, the shorter the wavelength.

Of course, there's more to light than meets the eye. Physicists have discovered that light does a lot more than just help us to see. Most people think that light is what they see coming from a light source such as a bulb, a flame or the sun. And to an extent, they are right. Although these sources do radiate light, the light emitted goes far beyond what we can see. The light that most people think of as light—that which lets us see—is defined as *visible light*. What these people don't realize is that the visible light emitted from familiar sources actually falls within a tiny fraction of the full spectrum of light.

So what is the spectrum of light? Glad you asked.

Light is comprised of the electromagnetic radiation spectrum (EMR). Which is just a fancy way of referring to a range of light waves. The EMR breaks down the different wavelengths and categorizes light according to common properties. Scientists have grouped light into seven categories. This spectrum, as you can see in diagram 3.1, is comprised of different wave types: radio waves, microwaves, infrared waves, visible light waves, ultraviolet waves, x-ray waves and gamma waves.

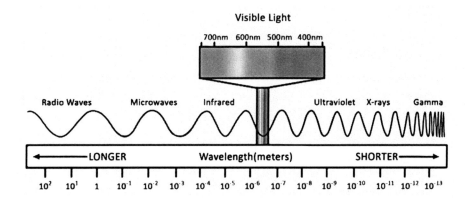

Diagram 3.1   The electromagnetic radiation spectrum of light

All of these waves are types of light, yet only visible light allows us to see objects. (Visible light is actually invisible. It is called *visible* because it makes other things visible to our naked eyes.) Since people don't use these terms every day, society has come to think of light as only what allows them to see. It's kind of like saying *Coke* to describe any soda. Further, since the light spectrum classifies light as waves, it is common to refer to light classifications as *waves,* such as *radio waves.* (It seems a little weird hearing them called *radio light,* but it means the same thing.)

To get an idea of how short a range visible light takes up on the entire EMR spectrum, imagine driving from Los Angeles, California to New York, New York. It would take less than 1 inch of your drive to travel the length of the visible light range. We tend to think that visible light is all there is to light, while in fact, the other light waves have a lot to do about what we call reality.

The electromagnetic spectrum is what science has currently been able to detect as the light spectrum. Science is fully aware that the spectrum could be even larger and consist of other light waves than are not understood at this time.

The light waves identified on the EMR exist throughout the universe. They are everywhere. Here on Earth, we are engulfed in radio light, microwave light, infrared light and visible light. Earth's atmosphere protects us from exposure to gamma light, x-ray light and most ultraviolet light. (However, we still need sunscreen to protect us from what the atmosphere misses.)

While visible light enables us to see things around us by reflecting off these things, the environment is filled with wavelengths of invisible light waves that our eyes cannot detect. Still, they are everywhere. Over the past couple hundred years, we've learned to harness these light waves to make our lives more convenient. Radios, microwave ovens, night-vision goggles and x-ray machines are just a few examples of tapping into the resources of the light spectrum.

We live in an illusion of reality. Yes, what we see around us is real. However, we seldom think about what is going on in the invisible realities. We tend to think we see all there is. We couldn't be more wrong. Not only is there an unseen world, but science tells us that there is vastly more going on in the invisible realms than the visible realm.

Quantum Electrodynamics

Let's get back to the hot-potato example and look closer at how light energy works with electrons. For anything in our world to occur—

for living things to breathe, grow and interact; for inanimate objects to combine, flow and decay—atoms must interact. Actually, it is the electrons of atoms which do most of the interacting, and this requires an ongoing supply of electromagnetic energy. When electrons interact, a phenomenon called *quantum electrodynamics* (QED) occurs where every instance of an interaction requires a photon of light to supply the electron with the needed energy. From the vast presence of the light waves of the EMR spectrum, a single photon converts from a wave to a particle, and engages with the electron to supply the needed energy.

Now, for any doubters out there, I can tell you that unlike many theories in quantum and string physics, QED has been tested many, many times with 100% accuracy. Not 20%; not 70%; not 90% ... 100% accurate! It is one of the great discoveries in human history.

Think of what this means. Every interaction between electron particles that occur in the entire universe, at every moment, involves light within the electromagnetic radiation spectrum. Not just visible light, but light from the entire spectrum. Science has discovered that light is everywhere at every moment in time, in other words, light is omnipresent! And it is an *active omnipresence,* meaning that it is involved with everything that occurs in the universe. Compare this with *passive omnipresence,* which means that something is present everywhere, but it may not be involved with everything occurring in the universe.

We are filled with light. Sure, people don't emit beams of light waves flashing off our bodies, but our bodies are filled with radio, infrared, microwave and ultraviolet light engaging with our every atom. Light is involved in every interaction of the hundreds of billions of interactions occurring every second in the human brain. In every brain neuron, every axon, every firing synapse, photons of light are actively, crucially involved— the same with all 7 billion people on the planet. Light plays an active role in every person's thought process at every moment. Brilliant!

Universal Super Glue

Light does more than illuminate our minds. Electromagnetism— light—is the force that helps the electrons of atoms bond together. In order for there to be different substances in the universe, such as rocks, water, salt and tandem bicycles, atoms need to bond together. But there are limitations to which atoms can bond and how many atoms can bond. The term *bond* becomes confusing because we tend to think from a materialistic perspective, like gluing two pieces of wood together.

Neglecting the chemical specifics for brevity, think of atoms joining together like a giant jigsaw puzzle, with each atom having a certain shape that allows it to fit with other atoms. Only certain atoms with the right shapes will snap together with each other. For example, a sodium (Na) atom will bond with a chlorine (Cl) atom to make sodium chloride (NaCl), known as table salt.

Having multiple atom puzzle pieces fitting together is only the first step needed in the process. Using our jigsaw puzzle analogy, imagine you completed a puzzle on the dining room table. All the pieces are fitted together, but now you want to lift the puzzle off the table. You will discover quickly that the joined pieces will not stay together under all circumstances. They fit together, but they are not bonded. Lifting the puzzle off the table will cause pieces to fall apart and incense whoever put the puzzle together in the first place.

Similarly, something greater than interlocking atomic shapes is needed to keep atoms together, and that is where light comes in. Atoms bond to other atoms by way of joining their electrons using energy provided by electromagnetic force, which is a form of light. (Not to be confused with the strong nuclear force, which bonds protons and neutrons in the nucleus of an atom). The various atoms that comprise the molecules of a brick, for instance, are bonded together at their electrons by electromagnetism.

Speaking of bricks, most people think the reason they can't walk through a brick wall is because their atoms are blocked by the brick atoms. As with most common understanding however, this thinking is scientifically incorrect. Remember what an atom looks like? They have a nucleus in the middle with electrons orbiting around the outside (diagram 1.1). In actuality, there is a tremendous amount of open space between the nucleus and the electrons. To give you a visual idea of how much room, if you were to enlarge the nucleus of an atom to the size of a Titleist Pro golf ball (*product placement*—you gotta love it), the electrons orbiting the nucleus would be about three miles away. In reality, most of the space atoms occupy is empty space.

So if running into the brick atoms is not the problem, what is? The strength of the bricks actually comes from electromagnetism. Light is what holds atoms together and prevents people from walking through the brick wall.

To understand this even better, let's try a handy demonstration. Place your palms together and press. Notice that your hands are being prevented from going through each other. Now consider this: the force stopping your hands is electromagnetism. The tension you feel is an increase in light energy being engaged with the electrons in each of your hands, stopping them from moving through each other. It is not the atoms in your hands that are preventing you from melding your two hands into a single flipper. It is light.

If it weren't for electromagnetism, there would not be much of anything preventing one hand from going through the other, or someone walking through a wall. But then again, without electromagnetism, the atoms could not bond in the first place, so there would be no brick wall. (*There is no spoon.*)

Every substance around us is held together by light. If it weren't for light, there would be no stars, planets, people, books, ink, gnats, or politicians... nothing. Light is the universal glue. The universe would not exist without it.

God is Light

Now let's bring God into the picture. The Bible has many passages directly associating God with light. Most Christians, untrained in science, don't give much thought to these passages, other than to think that light represents good and darkness represents evil. And yet, the issue of light is one of the most important connections between God and science. So let's not make light of the matter.

Recalling our visible light wave within the electromagnetic radiation spectrum, it is imperative to broaden the scope of God's light beyond the narrow, visible range, and include what science knows to be the entire range of light waves, including, radio, microwave, infrared, ultraviolet, x-ray and gamma waves of light. For example:

> *The LORD was going before them in a pillar of cloud by*
> *day to lead them on the way, and in a pillar of fire by night*
> *to give them light, that they might travel by day and by night.*
>
> *Exodus 13:21*

> *From the brightness before Him coals of fire were*
> *kindled.*
>
> *II Samuel 22:13*

Scientifically, visible light does not produce fire, heat does. The fire in the pillar of fire and the coals of fire are a result of infrared light waves— invisible light on the electromagnetic radiation spectrum. On Earth, fire is produced if infrared light waves, are involved. (Infrared light waves are what provide the heat.) Although there is visible light (and small amounts of radio, microwave, ultra-violet and x-ray) involved with fire, most of the light falls in the infrared range.

Earlier we discussed that, according to quantum physics, our bodies are full of light. To be more specific, we are primarily full of radio, microwave and infrared light, with trace amounts of visible and ultraviolet light. With that in mind, consider scriptures such as these:

> *Then Jesus again spoke to them, saying, "I am the*
> *Light of the world; he who follows Me will not walk in the*
> *darkness, but will have the Light of life,"*
>
> *John 8:12*

> *But if we walk in the Light as He Himself is in the Light,*
> *we have fellowship with one another,*
>
> *l John 1:7*

I propose that these scriptures are addressing the entire spectrum of light, not just visible light. We will see this unpacked more in further discussion.

People have a habit of pigeonholing definitions of words. Take the word *snow* for example. To most people, snow is light, white flakes of frozen water vapor. We love it or hate it, depending on whether we are skiing or digging out our car. However, the native Eskimos, who live with snow 10 months a year, have 50 different words for the stuff, each with a different connotation.

Let's think like enlightened people and not pigeonhole the definition of *light*. When the Bible—as well as science—considers light, there are many connotations for this vital energy. It's not just what keeps you from stubbing your toes on your way to the kitchen at midnight—*illumination*. The Hebrew and Greek languages have many meanings for *light*, especially when used in reference to God or Jesus Christ. The Hebrew language broadens the meaning to include: *all light diffused (that's every light, everywhere), glory, life, instruction and prosperity.* The Greeks have variations of light as well, including: *glory, brightness, magnificence, excellence, truth, knowledge, spiritual purity, reason, mental clarity and a separate kingdom of light.*

As we can see, Hebrew and Greek meanings for light go beyond the scientific realm of EMR. These languages give light added depth, associating it with life, prosperity, truth, knowledge and spiritual purity.

In the Psalms, David informs us that in God's light is a fountain of life.

> *For with You is the fountain of life; In Your light we see light...*
>
> *Psalm 36:9*

David further declares,

> *The LORD is my light and my salvation; whom shall I fear? The LORD is the defense of my life; whom shall I dread?*
>
> *Psalm 27:1*

> *Then Moses said, "I pray You, show me Your glory!"... But He said, "You cannot see My face, for no man can see Me and live!" Then the LORD said, "Behold, there is a place by*

Me, and you shall stand there on the rock; and it will come about, while My glory is passing by, that I will put you in the cleft of the rock and cover you with My hand until I have passed by. Then I will take My hand away and you shall see My back, but My face shall not be seen."

Exodus 33:18, 20-23

In these Bible verses, light clearly means more than sunlight. Although I make distinct correlations between the biblical God and science, we need to be careful to understand that the whole essence of God goes much deeper then these assertions. It is important to point out that God and Christ are often described as *light*. Here is an example:

When Jesus spoke again to the people, he said, "I am the light of the world. Whoever follows me will never walk in darkness, but will have the light of life."

John 8: 12

Of course, I am not in any way implying that God is limited to only being light. The Bible proclaims that God and Christ are more than light, and that light is a facet of both.

Is God an Impossibility? Or Omnipresent?

Even though the scope of the electromagnetic radiation spectrum was not known thousands of years ago when the stories in the Bible were first told, I've revealed a portion of the ample evidence that *light* means more than what we see with our eyes. Although there is a scientific depth to light that has been overlooked for centuries, science is now helping us understand how God can be so actively involved with His creation.

The Bible says God is omnipresent, that He is everywhere at all times. In Psalms, David writes,

Where can I go from Your Spirit? Or where can I flee from Your presence? If I ascend to heaven, you are there; if I make my bed in Sheol, behold, you are there.

Psalm 139:7

The Bible goes so far as to have passages quoting God himself as having the ability to be omnipresent. In the book of Job, God has a conversation with a man named Job, where God asks him if he has God's ability of omnipresence. Here is a brief excerpt:

> *Do you know the time the mountain goats give birth?*
> *Do you observe the calving of the deer? Can you count the*
> *months they fulfill, or do you know the time they give birth?*

Job 39:1- 2

Herein lies one of the connections between science and God that forever changed my life. I hope you understand its significance as well.

Through quantum electrodynamics (QED), science has proven that light is omnipresent. Light is everywhere, at all times. It has to be. It holds the universe together. Now, if God is light (as the Bible indicates), then science has proven that God is omnipresent—everywhere, at all times. Recall our discussion that light is vital to our thought process. If God is light, then God is present at every one of our thoughts, as defined by axons, dendrites and synapse firings. God is actively present with every thought of every person on the planet at every moment of every day. If God is light, then God cannot be some passive, lifeless, inert entity that created the universe and left it on its own. No. Science has proven that God can be an active, involved, dynamic God.

Let that sink in for a moment.

Conclusion

If God is real and created the universe, including all the laws of physics, then it would make sense that God would both create the universe and sustain it. I began this chapter by discussing the importance of light. Science proves that the universe can't exist without light. The Bible claims that God is active through light.

Is it just a wild coincidence that God, as light, just happens to coincide with the scientific fact that light is needed for atoms to bond together, for thoughts to occur, for the universe to exist—that God could be, in a word, *omnipresent?* Of all the things the Bible could use to describe God, it chooses *light* as one of the major aspects of God. Certainly, this doesn't prove that God exists, but it makes a compelling case that God *can* exist and be everything the Bible describes him as being. If God is light, then science supports the possibility that God could exist as light.

Chapter 4

~~~~~~

Quantum Discovers
New Realms of Reality

The preceding chapter on quantum electrodynamics (QED) laid the groundwork for our further studies. Hopefully, this is better than high-school biology. Now let's get into even more interesting phenomena.

Enlightenment

Imagine we are standing in a room that is completely dark; you can't see me and I can't see you. It's so dark that you can't even see yourself. I wave to you, you wave to me, but neither of us sees the other. In a sense, we are invisible. Then someone turns on the light from a switch outside the room and voila! We see each other. We have moved from an invisible state to a visible state, and the transitioning agent is light. This sounds simple until I tell you this is how the universe works.

An interesting phenomenon that occurs at the tiny sub-atomic state is a thing called the *wave/particle duality principle.*

Recall our discussion in Chapter 2 where we said light changes it's state depending on its interactions with light grabbing particles such as electrons. In our hot-potato example, we learned that electrons are in a constant state of either acquiring or releasing photons. Both electrons and photons are constantly changing state from a wave-state to a particle-state. In one instant, an electron may be in an invisible wave state, and without warning, change into a visible particle state. It's as though everything that makes up the universe alternates between opposite realities: Dr. Jekyll and Mr. Hyde, Democrats and Republicans, dogs and cats living together, mass hysteria! The discovery of this duality has rocked science's paradigm and forever altered our perceptions of reality.

For years, physicists debated whether the parts of atoms existed as waves or particles. Then Thomas Young, through his famous double-slit experiment, (breakdowns available on Youtube) discovered that photons of light and subparts of atoms (such as electrons) exist in what is called a *superposition*, meaning they can act as either a wave or a particle, depending... The question is: depending on what?

Before we answer that question, however, let's be clear on definitions:

Regarding sub-atomic particles, there really are not very many of them. There are only 17 fundamental particles (18 if you include the graviton) in the entire universe! If you want to get technical, we can include the variations some of these particles come in. Physicists call these variations colors, which would give a grand total of 37 (including the graviton), but for simplicity's sake, we'll keep to quantum's standard model of fundamental particles, which is 17, plus the graviton makes 18. And in regards to what we experience here on Earth, everything that is comprised of matter, for the most part, is comprised of only— get this—three different particles: *up quarks, down quarks* and *electrons*. Nearly everything you can think of: hydrogen, helium, gold, lead, the cells of your body, the fleas on your dog, are all made up of these three components of matter. That's it!

Nine of the remaining fundamental particles are under the general heading *fermions*. They are: *charm quarks, strange quarks, top quarks, bottom quarks, muons, taus, electron neutrinos, muon neutrinos* and *tau neutrinos*. We don't experience these in our everyday life. Five other particles make up the force carrier particles. They are *gluons, photons, W bosons, Z bosons and* the *Higgs boson*.

The last particle is the graviton, the black sheep of the family, because it doesn't work in quantum mechanics. (It works in the universe, because we have gravity, but it doesn't fit the quantum model.) One final note: particles have an opposite particle called an *anti-particle*. For example, the electron has an anti-particle called a *positron*, but anti-particles don't play much of a role in everyday life, and so we will not consider them further in our discussion.

Additional Realms

Recall our description of superposition in Chapter 3, where we said that photons exist as waves or particles. Now let's build on this understanding. Light is not the only thing that can exist in a superposition; basically, all the subatomic particles (electrons, protons, neutrons, quarks, etc.) that make up what we see and touch, exist in two states. However, to avoid confusion, we have to get a few terms straight.

We refer to the two states in which a particle can exist as: 1) *particle state,* or 2) *wave state.*

The *particle state* is when the particles exist in a way that we can see and touch them. Science calls this condition *local,* because the particles are present as an observable and measurable substance. Think of an electron in the particle state like a billiard ball. It is hard, you can touch it, see it and it bounces off the bumpers and other balls. A sub-atomic particle in particle state is just that: a particle.

The *wave state* is when subatomic particles are waves oscillating in space. You can't see or touch them. Science refers to this condition as *non-local* because the particles are invisible and can't be located, measured or observed... but they *do* exist. However, they exist in a non-detectable realm. Essentially, scientists don't know where they are. The weird thing about waves is they have the ability to exist anywhere in the universe. Science further calls this a *probability wave state* because, although a particle in the wave state can be anywhere in the universe, scientists can calculate the most probable location of those particles. Like tracking your teenager's phone with a poor GPS. You know she's in the mall, but exactly which store is anybody's guess.

So, to summarize: *particle state* is when a particle is acting like.... well, a particle. And *wave state* is when a particle is acting like a wave. At times, for clarity, I'll refer to either a *wave-state particle,* or a *particle-state particle.*

When particles are in the particle state, scientists are able to observe and measure them to discover things like how they work and the construction of the molecules they form. We call this observable realm *reality*. Still, science has discovered there are many other realities existing in the non-local realm (wave state); these are realms in which science can't observe and measure...at least, not yet.

While it is limiting to know we can't see things in wave state, it is also liberating to realize such a state(s) even exists. Therefore, when classical science claims that reality is all we can see with our senses, they are incorrect. And so is anyone who bases their conclusions on this outdated mode of discovery. Modern reality includes the undetected waves that are present throughout the universe.

So why can't scientists detect a particle's location when it is in wave form? This is what Schrodinger's cat and Heisenberg's *uncertainty principle* are all about. Using precise calculations, science can predict the most likely place where a particle will likely show up. But no one knows exactly where a particle is when it's a wave, so they can't say exactly where it will be when it collapses into particle form until it actually collapses. Whoever is clever enough to figure out how to observe particles in a wave state will certainly win a Nobel Prize.

Abracadabra

The double-slit experiment showed that at the super-small particle size, things like electrons, photons and their friends exist in the undetectable wave state until they are transitioned (or collapsed) into a detectable, particle state. Because all matter in the detectable universe is made up of atoms, this means everything we see and touch must somehow go through this transition phase to be detectable. Scientists have studied this phenomenon for a hundred years and have never been able to divert from this fact.

According to the wave/particle duality principle, whatever does not get collapsed will not become detectable (or localized). Remember the dark room. Something has to turn on the light switch. Similarly, the transition from wave state to particle state does not happen randomly. Something has to transition the particles from the non-detectable, non-local realm to the detectable, local realm. The non-local realm exists, but it does not exist in our realm until it exists locally.

Weird, I know. It is there…but it is *not* there…until it is there.

The Observer

For a better image of this, consider that the space around you is filled with invisible radio waves. (Recall that radio waves are light in the non-visible part of the EMR spectrum.) These waves are undetectable to our native senses. They exist in a realm where we can't see them or hear them, but we know they exist. How do we know? Because people have invented a transitioning agent called the radio which transitions the invisible, soundless waves into music, news or War of the Worlds. In order to hear sound, the waves must go through a transitioning agent such as a radio. Of course, the device doesn't transition all the radio waves in the room at once—that would be chaos. It only transitions the waves it is tuned for.

The transitioning of particles from undetectable to detectable states is similar in concept. If nothing transitioned the radio waves into sound, there would be no sound, but the radio waves would still exist. The same is true with subatomic particles such as up quarks, down quarks and electrons. They can't become localized particles on their own. They require a transitioning agent.

The double-slit experiment that discovered wave/particle duality, did so by observing the action of particles as they passed through a barrier wall with two-slits. When there was no measuring device, or when the device was inactive, the particles remained in a wave state. When the measuring device was turned on and measured the particles, they changed to a localized, particle state. Scientists concluded that it was the act of observation—the observing phenomenon—that collapsed a particle from a wave state to a particle state. They called it the *observer effect*.

The observer effect doesn't mean that someone can look at an electron and collapse it to a particle. The machines that observed and measured the particles in the double-slit experiments used beams of light within the electromagnetic radiation spectrum (see diagram 2). As the particles were observed and measured by use of light beams, they transitioned into a localized particle.

Through this experiment and others, science discovered that light allows particles to move from one state of existence into another state of existence—they discovered the transitioning agent! Although some people claim that consciousness or human observation can cause waves to collapse into particles, light is the only proven transitioning agent known to science that will transition particles from the non-local realm (wave state) into the local realm (particle state) of our four-dimensional world.

Where is it?

As scientists search for answers, they are ending up with more and more questions. For example: Where is the particle located before it collapses? Scientists want to know where a particle-wave is located while in the non-local realm before it transitions into the local realm. So far, physicists can predict the possible locations a particle-sate particle will show up, but they cannot pinpoint the exact location until the transition occurs. This is called the *measurement problem*.

It's like this. I am thinking of a number between 1 and 100. What is the number? You know that there is a 1% chance the number is 23, or any other number between 1 and 100. The only way to know the number exactly is to see it when I reveal it. But what if you could figure out and know the number is 23 before it is revealed? What if you could know the location of a particle while it is in the wave state? This is one of the objectives driving quantum physics today. The ramifications of figuring out the specific position of a particle while it is in the wave state, before it collapses to the particle state, are huge. (Think of picking winning lottery numbers.)

The Final Frontier

Do you ever wish you could go to the moon? What if I told you that part of you has? It's true. Part of you has been there many times and part of you may be there right now. I'm not saying that in the next two minutes, you will completely dematerialize here on Earth and re-materialize on the moon, although there is an infinitesimally remote possibility that you could. (Beam me up, Scotty!) The fact is that atoms do leave people and even leave Earth.

Because the sub-atomic parts comprising atoms exist as either invisible probability waves or visible particles, we don't know the exact location of the electrons orbiting the nucleus. Physicists can predict the most likely places to find an electron of an atom; it is usually close to its host atom. However, since electrons exist as probability waves before they collapse to particles, scientists have proven that a pre-collapsed electron exists everywhere in the universe, including on the moon at this very moment, even though you are sitting here on Earth. And since there is a probability that when an electron collapses to a particle it will do so outside the normal orbital range, means there are electrons in your body with a possible presence at the center of the Earth; the other side of the world; the other side of the universe. Therefore, we are never completely in one place at any given time. No wonder it's so hard to get it together on Monday mornings!

Science has proven that your existence goes beyond your physical body. Although there is a 95% probability an electron will collapse to a particle near its host atom, there is a 5% probability that it won't be near its atom. Which means some of you (and me, for that matter) is spread throughout the ends of the universe.

All atoms act in a similar fashion, continuously.

Where's the Rest of the Universe?

Look around you. What you see and touch—what we think of as real—is an infinitesimal fraction of what really exists. To see this, let's lay some groundwork. Physics says that no new energy or matter has come into the existence of the universe since the big bang. In addition, Conservation of Energy says that the universe can't lose the current total of energy and matter. That means if you add up all the energy and matter of the four forces of nature, along with all the stars, planets, space dust, gases and Beatles records in the entire universe, it would equal the same amount as at the moment of the big bang. And in another five billion years, it would still equal the same amount.

Of course, physicists are the inquisitive sort, so they added up all the energy and matter in the detectable universe, and that's when they ran into a little problem. They only found 5% of all matter and energy in the universe. (*Honey, I'll be working late tonight.*)

Yes, you read that right. Scientists can't find 95% of all matter and energy in the universe. They can only find 5% of it. Where's the rest of it? They know it is there, but it is undetectable. Science knows there is 20-times more energy and matter in our universe than the total of all the stars, planets, black holes, nebulae, quasars and energy. It's somewhere out there, causing all of us to scratch our heads and wonder.

This leads to an astounding conclusion. In order for the universe to exist as it does, additional undetectable matter and energy must exist—*lots* of it. Imagine how exciting and yet frustrating this dilemma is for scientists. It is exciting to know there are realities beyond what we see and touch, but frustrating because science does not know how to observe these other realities. Scientists decided to call this undetectable stuff *dark matter* and *dark energy.*

Could this dark matter and dark energy exist in parallel universes or in additional dimensions? Are there other forms of matter—wave-based perhaps, comprising alternate life forms? Angels maybe? Are wave-based creatures staring into the void presented by a particle-based reality, wishing they could study particles if only they could find them?

Time will tell.

Just Get Real!

Although some of the world's best scientists are looking for undetectable dark matter energy, the majority of scientists are studying what is occurring in the localized particle state. After all, it is easier to study observable things than that which remains tantalizingly undetectable.

But, as often happens in scientific inquiry, all this understanding leads to a broader question looming over the physics world.

According to the wave/particle duality principle, to be observable, matter must go through a transitioning agent and collapse from a wave state into a particle state. Further, if invisible waves are not transitioned (through observation/measurement), they must remain in the non-local wave state. Since we know we currently exist in a localized particle realm comprising 5% of the matter and energy created at the big bang, then we know that a transitioning agent had to occur, causing the 5% become detectable matter and energy. And it had to occur somewhere between today and the big bang—a span of 13.8 billion years.

So here's the question: What caused our universe to transition from an undetectable wave state into our reality of a detectable particle state? What turned on the light in the room? And when did this happen? And why only 5% of all matter and energy—the sum total of the detectable universe?

Although light is exclusively used in experiments to collapse waves to particles, the scientific community does not have a proven theory for how light or any other agent could act as the transitioning agent and cause the universe to transition to a particle position. It is one thing to use light as a medium in experiments; it is quite another thing to explain how light could choose which waves will collapse into a particle state and which waves will remain in wave state. It would be easy if all light collapsed all waves to particles. Unfortunately, our universe isn't that simple. Science needs an explanation as to how and why light sometimes collapses waves and sometimes doesn't.

At this point, science doesn't even have one possible theory that has gained the majority support in the scientific community. Interestingly, the New Age movement exploded in popularity in the 1970's largely from trying to solve the observer effect dilemma. New Age believes there is a cosmic consciousness that is performing the observer effect. Voila! An answer that explains how the universe exists in a localized particle state. Of course, it isn't supported by scientific experiments, but many people subscribe to this manmade interpretation anyway.

The Bible has an Explanation

The Bible has numerous accounts of unseen realms. Remarkably, the Bible claims that God is involved with both the invisible and the visible realms. Here are a couple Biblical references that support this.

> *For by Him all things were created, both in the heavens and on earth, visible and invisible, whether thrones or dominions or rulers or authorities—all things have been created through Him and for Him.*
>
> *Colossians 1:16*

> *By faith we understand that the worlds were prepared*
> *by the word of God, so that what is seen was not made out of*
> *things which are visible.*
>
> *Hebrews 11:3*

Genesis Transition Story

No human document in mankind's history has gone into as much detail describing the observer effect—transitioning from the non-local wave realm to the localized particle realm—as the book of Genesis. From a quantum perspective, Genesis is the most important ancient scientific document in the history of mankind.

If you have never read Genesis, it is easy to find in the Bible. It begins on page one. *"In the beginning God..."* The first two chapters of Genesis are commonly referred to as the creation story. Later, we will focus more on the issue of creation as described in Genesis. For now, we are specifically concentrating on the observer effect. From a quantum perspective, Genesis is not only a creation story, it is also the transitioning agent story. The opening of Genesis could be paraphrased to read: *"In the beginning, the Transitioning Agent..."*

Before we get too far, let's first establish that the Bible declares that a non-detectable condition existed. Genesis Chapter 1, verses 1 and 2, describe in detail the universe in an undetectable, invisible state.

> *In the beginning, God created the heavens and the earth.*
> *And the earth was formless and void, and darkness was over*
> *the face of the deep; and the Spirit of God was hovering over*
> *the face of the waters.*
>
> *Genesis 1:1-2*

There are some important words in this passage to dissect and understand from a quantum perspective. First, in the Hebrew language, and the context for this passage, *formless* refers to *empty space*. In addition, *void* means *emptiness*, or *vacuity* (*without physical existence*). So on the one hand, the text says the universe exists, and on the other hand, it says it is without physical existence.

Here are some other important word meanings in the context of their use:

- *created*—produced, cut down, brought into existence

- *heavens*—expanse of space that seems to be over the earth like a dome

- *darkness*—absence of light, the dark, not receiving or reflecting, transmitting or radiating light

- *deep*—vast depth, chasm, far into or below the surface of something

- *Spirit of God*—energy of life, by which all the universe is animated, filled with life and governed

- *hovering*—to brood over, rapid back and forth movement

Now let's look at Genesis 1:1-2 again, but from a scientific perspective.

In the beginning, God created the expanse of space over the earth and the earth. And the earth was empty space, and having no physical existence, and the absence of light was over the surface of the vast depth; and the energy of life remained suspended over the surface moving to and fro over the surface of the waters.

Hopefully, you can see that from a quantum perspective, the first two verses of Genesis align with the wave/particle duality Principle of quantum physics. The universe is described as being there, but without a physical presence. It is undetectable.

The Genesis passage explains there was only darkness *In the beginning.* As we learned earlier, light can act as an observer agent. Without the observer agent of light being active, the universe must be in an undetectable state. And according to Genesis, it *is* in an undetectable state. Just as in the scenario of being in the dark room with the lights turned off—without light as an observer agent—the universe is invisible.

In Chapter 3, I explained that the Bible describes an aspect of God as being light. Not only does light play an integral role with supplying energy to all matter in the observable universe, light has also been proven to be the only known substance to qualify as an observer agent. If God is light, and light qualifies as an observer agent, let's see what happens when light enters the scene of the Genesis creation story.

While the first two verses of Genesis describe the universe in a non-detectable state, the rest of the first chapter describes the transition from the non-detectable wave state, to a detectable particle state. Let's move on to what Genesis describes next and see how the Bible addresses one of the most sought-after questions in the quantum science disciplines: How and when did the universe transition from a non-localized wave state to a localized particle state?

> *Then God said, "Let there be light" and there was light.*
> *And God saw that the light was good; and God separated the*
> *light from the darkness.*

> *Genesis 1:3-4*

Let's examine the key words in this passage. It does not say, *"God created..."* the Bible already declared in Genesis 1:1-2 that God created everything. Here in verses 3 and 4, we read, *"God said...."* The Hebrew meaning of *said* is: *declared, commanded.*

Some of the other important words to understand are these:

- *let*—to uncover, to expose, to extend, render

- *saw*—cause to, make to, perceive, appear

- *light*—light everywhere diffused, being everywhere at once

When understood from the context of these words, the Genesis passage describes a process where God *sees (causes to, perceives, appears)* a portion of the undetectable realm and *appoints it, declares it to be exposed, to be extended, to be rendered.*

Here is what Genesis 1:3-4 sounds like when interpreted from a scientific perspective.

> *Then God declared, "Render all light everywhere," and*
> *all the light was everywhere. And God observed all the light*

that was everywhere was good; and God separated all the light everywhere from the absence of light.

Is it a coincidence that the writer of Genesis used the word *saw* in this passage? On the surface, it seems like it doesn't have much importance at all. And yet it does, explaining one of the most puzzling questions in all of physics. Science is looking for an observer agent, and within the pages of an ancient document is a cohesive description of just such an agent in the creation of the universe as we understand it.

People who believe God created the universe, and who also accept the big bang, tend to think that the light on the first day was the blast from the big bang. While that may be true, it appears that the light on the first day in Genesis is actually describing the observer effect required by quantum physics—the imperative for the universe to come into a visible, detectable existence.

The first action God took in the transitioning process was to deal with light. According to quantum physics, without an observer agent such as light, everything that existed in the non-local wave state would remain in that condition, and therefore, nothing would exist as we know it. In order for the observer effect to occur, light had to come first. Of all the possible descriptions to choose from, the writer of Genesis chooses the only possible explanation that just happens to align with the quantum principle of the observer effect. Wow!

The Rest of the Story

This process of *seeing* the universe into a localized existence is repeated throughout Genesis Chapter 1. There are five specific instances described in detail during this passage where God *said* (*declared*), *let* (*uncovered, rendered*) and *saw* (*to appear*), affecting the waters, land, plants, trees, stars, fish, birds, animals and humans. The important concept here is that according to quantum physics, these things already existed, they just didn't exist in a visible particle state.

In Genesis, only five of the days declare that God *saw* that it was good. Interestingly, there is one day in the Genesis creation story where the writer does not say that God *saw* that it was good. Was this an oversight? This could pose a problem, because now the Bible would not align with the quantum observer effect on this day. And, according to the observer effect, this would mean that the contents of that day would not transition into a detectable, particle state, and in essence, must still be in an undetectable, non-local state.

The day that does not say God *saw* was the second day, which was the day describing the heavenly realm. I don't know about you, but I can't see a visible heavenly realm (except for the day I met my wife). But instead of a problem arising, the Bible actually nails it from a quantum physics perspective because in the many biblical accounts of a heavenly realm, it all exists in an invisible, undetectable state.

Turn on the Lights

There have been many debates between scientists, evolutionists, creationists and theologians over the context of the Genesis account, specifically in regards to the position of an old Earth vs. young Earth. Scientists and evolutionists use scientific data to claim that the universe is 13.8 billion years old and the Earth is 4.5 billion years old. Some creationists, based on their interpretation of the Bible, claim the Earth is 6,000 to 10,000 years old. The two opinions could not be further apart. However, when we read the Genesis story from a quantum perspective, we find the two viewpoints are able to coexist.

In the bizarre world of quantum physics, the universe is real, but it is not real until it is real. This speaks to two realities of existence. The first reality is what scientists describe as the big bang, which occurred 13.8 billion years ago. Quantum theory has proven that the universe without a transitioning agent would exist in an invisible, non-local wave-state. As such, it would still be real, but not as we consider *real*. Since we can see and touch the world around us, we know that something is causing the non-local, wave-state particles to become local, particle-state particles. This reveals the second reality of existence, which is based on interpreting Genesis as the detailed process of the universe transitioning from the invisible to the visible. Hence, the universe as we know it was not real until it became real.

*By faith we understand that the worlds were prepared
by the word of God, so that what is seen was not made out of
things which are visible.*

Hebrews 11:3

Since science doesn't have a proven theory for a transitioning agent that acted on the universe, science can't prove how or when the universe came into existence as an observable, localized particle-state. Still, from a quantum physics perspective, the Genesis story presents an accurate depiction of the transitioning process and timeline. The Bible tells us that God brought forth everything we see in a six-day period. First, the universe existed, but in a non-local, undetectable wave state. Then the universe transitioned to what we experience today—a local, detectable particle state.

Picture a house with over a million Christmas lights. They are beautifully arranged and cover the house, the trees, the front lawn, the front fence, the swimming pool—every square centimeter has Christmas lights decorating it. The owner of the house took 11 months to hang all the lights. When it is finally Christmas time, the owner gathers all his neighbors to share in the celebration of unveiling his masterpiece. Except, instead of turning on all the lights at once, the owner flips the switches one at a time, revealing the house, then the lawn, then the trees, the pond and so on, until everything was illuminated.

The lights existed in two states, one with the lights off and another with the lights on. Now, did the lights exist when they were off? Of course they did. However, from the perspective of the neighbors, the delight of the lights was not real until they were turned on.

We now have a scientific means to resolve the questions of how and when did the universe transition from waves to particles, as well as settling any potential discrepancies between the development between the big bang and Genesis. The order of the collapsing wave functions to particles does not have to be in the same order as scientists propose occurred over the 13.8 billion year development since the big bang (see chapter 2).

I Spy With my Little Eye

Through Genesis Chapter 1, we have established a connection between quantum physics and the Bible regarding the observer agent.

However, according to quantum physics, the observer agent would need to continuously act as an observer agent for the detectable universe to remain detectable. Recall that sub-atomic particles are constantly changing state: particle to wave; wave to particle. To verify God as an observer agent, the Bible would have to make additional claims that God continues to be the observer agent. And indeed, the Bible makes it clear that God did not stop *seeing* at the end of the six days of transitioning. There are many verses that describe God as continually seeing His creation.

This makes sense when we consider our previous conclusion that God can be omnipresent through light because light is everywhere at all times. Light is the key to acting as an observer agent. Here are a few Bible verses depicting God's ability to see:

> But the Lord said to Samuel, "Do not look at his appearance or at the height of his stature, because I have rejected him; for <u>God sees not as man sees</u>, for man looks at the outward appearance, but the Lord looks at the heart."
>
> I Samuel 16:7 (underline added)

> For He < God > looks to the ends of the earth and <u>sees everything under the heavens</u>. When He imparted weight to the wind and meted out the waters by measure, when He set a limit for the rain and a course for the thunderbolt, then He saw it and declared it; He established it and also searched it out.
>
> Job 28:24-27 (underline added)

> And there is <u>no creature hidden from His < God's > sight</u>, but all things are open and laid bare to the eyes of Him with whom we have to do.
>
> Hebrews 4:13 (underline added)

To remain within the objective of this study, we will leave the theology of why God sees (i.e., to love, to guide, to judge, etc.,) to theologians. From a scientific perspective, the use of God as light to cause non-localized waves to collapse and become localized particles is consistent with quantum physics.

According to quantum physics, if God is light, it is possible that God is the observer agent.

Finally, let's briefly address the topic of light in Genesis 1:3-4. Of day one, we read:

> *Then God said, "Let there be light" and there was light.*
> *And God saw that the light was good; and God separated the*
> *light from the darkness.*

In Genesis 1:14-16, the topic of light comes up again on day four.

> *And God said, "Let there be lights in the vault of the*
> *sky to separate the day from the night, and let them serve as*
> *signs to mark sacred times, and days and years, and let them*
> *be lights in the vault of the sky to give light on the earth."*
> *And it was so. God made two great lights—the greater light to*
> *govern the day and the lesser light to govern the night. He also*
> *made the stars.*

Why does the Bible describe the appearance of light on both day one and day four?

Studying the Hebrew, Genesis 1:3-4 describes light that is diffused everywhere. It is addressing the appearance of light in general—what science would describe as the electromagnetic radiation spectrum (and beyond). In Genesis 1:14-16, however, the Bible is describing luminaries— things which afford light, or things which light can come from, such as the sun and the stars.

I find it very interesting that the writer of Genesis made a distinction between the two descriptions of light. To the everyday reader, these distinctions don't mean much. However, in regard to quantum physics and how the non-local realm transitions to the local particle realm in the four dimensions we live in, these distinctions are tremendously important.

To Boldly Go

Science falls drastically short in explaining how the universe can be experienced as particles when every particle must be observed into existence. However, the Bible aligns beautifully with the observer effect experiments.

The books of the Bible describe, in great detail, God as the observer. The Bible incorporates the observer effect and transitioning from the non-local realm to the local realm better than any other written document in human history. This amazing ability to align with the quantum world is enough to claim that God is possible. But let's go to a place where no spiritual belief has gone before. Let's address the *delayed choice effect* and the *delayed choice quantum eraser effects*.

Come on. The fun is just beginning.

Chapter 5

Delayed Choice Quantum Eraser Effect – Omniscience

All scientists are clever, but some scientists are more clever than others. Physicist John Wheeler—a particularly clever individual—discovered a phenomenon called *the delayed choice effect.* In this famous experiment, Mr. Wheeler was able to devise a way to delay the outcome of the observer effect—the effect demonstrated by the double slit experiment.

As you recall, the original double-slit experiments employed light detectors focused at the particular location where the subatomic particles went through two slits in a barrier wall. With the light detectors activated, scientists were able to cause wave collapse to the particle state and determine which slit the test sample went though. When the detectors were not activated, the test samples remained as waves and did not collapse into particles. Scientists then concluded that the act of observing and/or measuring particles collapses the non-localized waves to become localized particles, units of our perceived reality. Yeah science!

Then along came physicist John Wheeler, who decided to place detectors at the end of the process to observe the particles, rather than at the slits like the original experiment. His findings changed how science understands reality. He discovered that the observing process determines the wave collapse, just as in the double slit experiment, but his findings went further. He found that the collapse seemed to occur retroactively, after the particles had traveled through the slits.

Even though Wheeler's detectors did not measure the particles until the end of the process, Wheeler still wanted to know if the particles traveled through the experiment as waves or as particles. Wheeler found (and it was later confirmed by Alain Aspect) that particles passing through the experiment would either remain waves or collapse to particles depending on whether the particles were observed at any time throughout the process, *including* at the end of the process. If there was no measurement, the particles would not collapse. However, if there was measurement, even at the end of the process, the particles would collapse into particles in the middle of the experiment—retroactively! To put it another way, the experiment showed that the particles delayed their collapse from wave to particle until they "knew" they were being observed at the end of the experiment.

The conclusion of Wheeler's experiment was that, somehow in the quantum world, our perception of reality can be delayed. What we thought was real actually changes retroactively, depending on how and when reality is perceived (or detected).

So what is delayed reality?

Let's say you owe your electricity bill and you decide to pay it old-school by writing a check and mailing it in. In the original double-slit experiment, with the observer detectors at the slits, our perceived reality of paying the bill occurs when the check is written. But Wheeler's delayed choice experiment says that our perceived reality is when the check clears the bank, and until it *does* clear the bank, the history of you writing the check and mailing it is unknown. A lot can happen between writing the check and clearing the bank. The check could be lost, your bank account could be depleted of funds, or the U.S. Postal Service could be late delivering the letter containing the check. (Not a chance!) And yet, all of these occurrences are subject to the check clearing the bank.

Wheeler said in his book: *The Ghost in the Atom* (page 66), "The past is not really the past until it is registered. Or put it another way, the past has no meaning or existence until it exists as a record in the past."

Until the moment the particle is observed, its past state, wave or particle, is subject to change. Of course, Wheeler said that a long time ago, in the past. But you are just reading it now.

Delayed Choice Quantum Eraser Effect

Not to be outdone, quantum physicists built upon Wheeler's experiment and took it further. They devised an experiment called *the delayed choice quantum eraser experiment,* which was much improved because it had a longer, fancier name. It also included prisms, mirrors, interferometers, more detectors and presumably a larger budget. In this complicated experiment, physicists were able to track numerous paths of photons within one experiment and decipher, without interfering in the process, when photons collapsed from waves to particles. Incredibly, they were able to prove that it is possible to erase the effects of a previous wave collapse through observation. Hence the *eraser* in the experiment's name. *Erasing wave collapse* is another way of stating Wheeler's conclusions, which is that perceived reality rewrites its own history based on observation.

They discovered that photons that originally went through the slits as waves, were collapsed to particles, and then somehow went back to their original wave state. In essence, whatever controls the knowledge or collection of data, controls if and when perceived reality occurs in our four-dimensional world. Professor Brian Greene describes it this way;

> "When the eraser is inserted just in front of the detector screen, it does — it erases — the effect of tagging the photons way back when they approached the slits. As in the delayed choice experiment, in principle this kind of erasure could occur billions of years after... in effect undoing the past, even undoing the ancient past!"
>
> *Fabric of the Cosmos,* Brian Greene page 193

These findings posed many problems for physicists. How do we know what is real? Can we trust our observations? What else is happening in our universe that we haven't discovered yet? Quantum physics declares two realities are occurring; what we see in our perceived particle-state reality is one thing and the realities of wave-state could be another.

No Broad Brush

The ramifications of these experiments are wide-reaching. Recall that any time we discuss collapsed particles, we are talking about our reality: what we see, hear, touch and smell. From these results, science is able to prove rather easily that people controlling an experiment can determine not only *whether* a wave collapses to a localized particle, but *when* it collapses. Further, if the particle had collapsed to a particle state, the collapse can be erased and the particle be made to appear as a wave. So a choice seems to be made to collapse or not collapse. And a choice can be made to go back in time and change the collapse. It means that non-localized waves do not necessarily collapse to detectable particles automatically or universally.

Science can't make a broad-brush claim that the presence of light is causing collapse everywhere. This is easily proven by the fact that you are currently surrounded by non-localized waves that have not been collapsed into a detectable particle state. The room you are in is filled with light waves (i.e. radio, microwave, infrared) that have not collapsed to photon particles. Even during double-slit experiments, light present in the room doesn't automatically collapse waves. The question is: Why have some waves collapsed and not others? Somehow, the universe has a way to determine when and which waves collapse into our perceived reality, and which waves remain as waves.

In addition to needing a transitioning agent as discovered in the double-slit experiments, Wheeler uncovered another key to wave collapse to be the collection and releasing of data. Humans can control the outcome of a wave collapse by collecting information on their computer and deciding to release the information or withhold it. Depending on the choice to release or withhold determines a wave-state or particle-state. Theoretically, the universe seems to have the same ability to control outcomes. Collecting information on a computer is one thing, what collection and releasing of data means in the cosmic sense science doesn't know.

At this point in time, physicists have discovered the phenomenon, they don't know how it occurs in the natural. What it does do is open the door for explanations. The universe has become a complicated process. Gone are the days of philosophies which do not take quantum physics into account. It is simply illogical to make universal suppositions without quantum considerations.

Eeny, Meeny, Miney, Moe

Fundamentally, we must ask: What chooses our observable, four-dimensional reality? And how is that reality determined? Well, the way the observer process actually occurs is still being sought by scientists. Many are so baffled by these questions they avoid them like the proverbial elephant in the room. Others have come up with theories, although no one can agree on a single theory. (I discuss some of the most notable theories in Chapter 9).

However, in the interest of completion (I started this line of inquiry; I should at least *try* to answer it), here is what quantum physicists have concluded so far:

1. The observer process is a vital factor in determining our reality as we know it—what is in it, and when it is in it.

2. That which we see, touch, smell and hear, transitions from an invisible, non-localized realm to our perceived reality.

3. That which we see, touch, hear and smell is not real until the observer process releases the reality.

4. That which we see, touch, hear and smell may be a different reality than what has occurred in the past—history is subject to change retroactively.

Push Play

Before you get too overwhelmed, this analogy might help. Let's say there is a show that has six seasons to it and you receive seasons 4-6 in a DVD set as a gift from a friend. You have never seen the show before, never heard anything about it and there is no information about the show. What is the reality of the show? It exists, but until you push play and release the data, it has no reality for you. The show exists – but it doesn't exist – until it exists. Welcome to quantum physics.

Now let's say you started on season 4. You start gaining understanding of the characters, relationships and the plot, however, if you don't start from the beginning of season 1, you don't know as much about the story as you could.

As you watch more episodes moving forward, you'll start to get remnants of information and piece together the past episodes that you missed. However, you won't be able to understand the full reality of those previous shows unless the data is revealed and you can watch those prior shows. Let's say you watch the show and learn that the main character John is single. In a later show, you find out that John has two children. You are given a remnant of the past (he has two children), but you don't know if John was previously married, if he had the children out of wedlock, if he is a widower, etc.

This is kind of what figuring out the universe is like; we picked up watching the universe in season 4. The problem is we don't have all the DVD's of the previous seasons, and so we have to piece together most of the past through the remnants found in the seasons that are being played. With our current technology, science is finding all kinds of remnants of previous seasons: homo erectus bones, dinosaur bones and fossils, development of Earth, age of stars, distant galaxies, etc. And there is so much of the unknown yet to be uncovered. Science is working hard to find ways to look at previous seasons.

Although many things are happening in the unseen wave-state realms, humans are mostly limited to the perceived realms of the particle-state. Still, our cleverness is allowing us to tap into the unseen realms and transfer some of the unseen into perceived reality. It is as though we are imitating the cosmic observer process. Take NASA's Wilkinson Microwave Anisotropy Probe (WMAP) for example. This probe, launched out into space in 2001, measured the Cosmic Microwave Background radiation (microwave light), revealing such world-changing facts as various temperatures throughout the universe and its age (13.8 billion years). For billions of years there was an unseen reality of microwave radiation throughout the universe until a process brought it into our perceived reality. Was it always there? Yes. It was always real. However, it wasn't real (our perceived reality) until it became real.

It is as though you watch the show and it suddenly becomes a different show. For centuries, scientists believed the universe always existed – that it did not have a beginning. The show changed when Edwin Hubble discovered that galaxies are moving away from each other and the universe is expanding. It has always been expanding, but our reality did not perceive it as so until it was revealed to us. I'd like to say that because of Hubble, our reality of the universe has forever been changed. However, something in the future may lie ahead that alters Hubble's expanding universe reality. In our limited world of perceived reality, we don't know the beginning of the story until we know the beginning of the story.

Universal Director and Editor

A lot goes into producing a show before it is available to the public. You have the writers, actors, camera people, etc. But the director and editor are in charge of bringing everything together to represent the final story. The director is responsible for how and what scenes are brought to the screen. It is up to the director and the editor to decide what stays and what is deleted.

The only way for us to be as real as we are--seeing, touching, smelling, tasting hearing *and* reading—is for non-local waves to collapse into localized particles. Because of the extraordinary discoveries of physicists like Wheeler, Aspect and Kim, we know that something or some process in the universe needs to be acting like a director and editor.

It is difficult to claim that random chance is the director that chooses which wave particles collapse into our reality and which wave particles remain as waves. This is because of the unity and consistency of localized particles found in our reality. For example, an apple is made up of a large number of detectable particles; which make up molecules, which make up cells... etc. Every one of the particles of the apple had to be collapsed from a non-detectable wave state. If random choice were acting as the observer agent (director), at the quantum level, there is no scientific or logical reason as to why the apple has the consistent form of an entire apple. In other words, if random chance acted as the observer there would be instances where large portions of apples would be missing because those portions randomly did not collapse the wave functions into localized particles.

The collapsing of waves into particles is not a one-time event. Electrons, protons, photons, etc. do not exist as particles forever once they get collapsed from a wave state. They continually transition back and forth between the wave state and particle state. For example, although our apple always looks like an entire apple, it is never in an "entirely" particle condition. This is because the atoms of the apple are continually going from a wave state to a particle state to wave state to particle state. It is happening so fast that to the naked eye no one notices. Neither classical nor quantum physics can answer how random chance is able to maintain the consistency of objects (i.e. the apple) as they go back and forth from waves to particles.

Not only does random chance have a problem with consistently collapsing and maintaining entire apples; it has to explain how it works within the 5% energy and matter of the observable universe. Everything we have discussed in this book has dealt with what scientists call the observable universe. This is a little bit of a misnomer because the observable universe consists of all the energy and matter that scientists can detect and that includes the invisible waves of energy in electrons, protons, electromagnetic radiation (EMR), etc. The observable universe is not everything that we can "see" in the universe. It might be easier to think of this 5% as the detectable universe, meaning it is everything we can detect through the use of all technological devices invented. In any event, 95% of energy and matter in the universe scientists can't detect. Again, this is what physicists call dark energy and dark matter. It is there... somewhere, but they can't find it yet.

How does random chance always collapse the correct 5% of the universe while not collapsing any of the undetectable portion of the universe? Scientists have discovered they have the ability to collapse electrons from a wave state to a particle state, however, they can't do it by random chance. It is always done under controlled conditions. At the quantum level, science does not have answers to how random chance can answer these issues.

The delayed choice and delayed choice quantum eraser experiments reveal that the realities of the world around us could possibly hang in a non-localized undetectable limbo for thousands, millions and even billions of years waiting to be collapsed into localized particles. According to Dr. Amit Goswami (*God is Not Dead*, Hampton Roads, 2008 pg104)

"The conclusion is inescapable. 'There ain't nothing' until an observer sees it: all objects remain in possibility, even macroscopic objects, until consciousness chooses from the possibilities and an event of collapse occurs. Then it all manifests, even retroactively."

Let's go back and revisit the Genesis transition theory. The delayed choice and delayed choice quantum eraser effect experiments provide evidence that supports the Genesis story of the Bible. If we interpret Genesis as describing the beginning of the universe, which includes the big bang through the creation of man, and if we further accept that the matter and energy released during the big bang existed in a non-localized state until God consciously "saw" it into existence, then both the big bang 13.8 billion years ago AND creation as described in Genesis some 6,000 – 50,000 years ago, could have occurred. This theory, as supported by quantum physics, allows the Bible to be consistent with science and support a creator God.

Omniscience

According to quantum physics, observing—or measuring—is not the only criteria needed to complete the observer effect process. The conclusion of the delayed choice and delayed choice quantum eraser discoveries is that whatever or however the observer agent operates, the process must have a way to obtain knowledge of each and every observation and have the ability to choose to release that knowledge. Otherwise, as in our apple example, there would be a lack of consistency in our observable universe. In short, the observer agent must have the ability to be all knowing—to have omniscience. Science does not have an answer for how this occurs in the universe.

We learned in Chapter 3 through quantum electrodynamics that light is omnipresent; it is everywhere, at every moment. Science has also discovered through experiments that light can act as the observer agent and collapse waves into localized particles. In fact, light is the only known agent to have the ability to collapse waves. Light is not only the best contender to fulfill the observer agent role, it is the only known possibility. Since light is omnipresent, it would make sense to examine light to find out if it has the ability to choose. Is there any scientific evidence that light has an ability to have knowledge or the ability to influence a particular outcome?

The answer is yes. Through the results of experiments in quantum electrodynamics, science does indeed associate light as more than a transferring agent of force; it is also understood to be something that has influence between the interactions of engaging particles. Brian Greene states (The Elegant Universe, pg. 124), "It's as if the photon [light] is not so much a transmitter of the force per se, but rather the transmitter of a message of how the recipient must respond to the force in question."

Somehow, light is involved in the outcome of every interaction between engaging particles, and is associated with having knowledge with interacting electrons.

God Meets the Criteria

It just so happens that the Bible claims that God knows all things. The Bible is full of passages claiming God's ability to be "all knowing." Here are a few examples:

> *Where then does wisdom come from? And where is the place of understanding? Thus it is hidden from the eyes of all living, And concealed from the birds of the sky. Destruction and Death say, 'With our ears we have heard a report of it.' God understands its way, And He knows its place. For He looks to the ends of the earth, And sees everything under the heavens. When He imparted weight to the wind, And meted out the waters by measure, When He set a limit for the rain, And a course for the thunderbolt, Then He saw it and declared it; He established it and also searched it out.*

> *Job 28:20-27*

> *It is He who reveals the profound and hidden things; He knows what is in the darkness, and the light dwells with Him.*

> *Daniel 2:22*

> *In whatever our heart condemns us; for God is greater than our heart and knows all things.*

> *1 John 3:20*

> *But of that day and hour no one knows, not even the angels of heaven, nor the Son, but the Father alone.*

> *Matthew 24:26*

God Chooses

The Bible is very clear on its position that God is aware of everything. The Bible also gives ample evidence that God decides what becomes real. In the earlier example of the Genesis transition theory, I associated God's light as the means by which God correlates with science to transitioning the non-local universe into a localized state. In the 38th Chapter of the Book of Job, the Bible gives a detailed account of God as the one who designed and maintains the universe. This is another Biblical correlation with modern science.

> *Then the* LORD *answered Job out of the whirlwind and said, "Who is this that darkens counsel by words without knowledge? Now gird up your loins like a man, And I will ask you, and you instruct Me! Where were you when I laid the foundation of the earth? Tell Me, if you have understanding, who set its measurements? Since you know. Or who stretched the line on it? On what were its bases sunk? Or who laid its cornerstone?"*

Job 38:1-6

If God is light (as the Bible describes), and light has the ability to have knowledge of interacting electrons, and light is everywhere, then God as light can be all knowing and present everywhere at all times. Further, if the Bible is correct and God, being light, has the ability to know all things and choose which electrons collapse into particles, it gives humanity a viable explanation for:

1. How categories of objects (i.e. apples) consistently appear as whole objects (apples always appear as whole apples),

2. How objects (i.e. apple) consistently maintain their entire form throughout their ongoing process of going back and forth between wave state and particle state,

3. How there is a determination between which of the 5% of the observable universe consistently exists.

As we get deeper and deeper into the bizarre world of quantum physics, the criteria needed to explain the observable universe is immense.

Here is a summary of what we've covered to this point. Science has discovered there is a non-localized, invisible realm that exists beside the physical localized realm we experience in our everyday life. To explain the reality of the world around us—what we can see, touch, smell and hear— science says we need a minimum of the following:

1. Omnipresence; something or some process has to be present everywhere, at every moment;

2. Observer agent; something or some process needs to be able to collapse waves into localized particles;

3. Omniscience; something or some process needs to have the ability to be everywhere and choose which waves collapse and which waves remain as waves.

The God of the Bible meets these strict criteria of science and the laws of physics. Unfortunately for those who believe in it, random chance falls short of meeting the criteria of the quantum world in every regard. Again, let me reiterate that I am not proving that God exists. I am making the case that God continually meets and exceeds the bizarreness of quantum mechanics, and offers better explanations than any other known scientific theory.

Chapter 6

~~~~~~~~~~~~~~~~~~~~~~~~~~~~~~~~

Vibration

The Sound of Music

Have you ever wondered why music is played in so many different forms and employed by every culture in history? Blaise Pascal wrote, "It is not those who write the laws that have the greatest influence on society, but those who write the songs." Plato penned, "Give me the music of a generation and I can change the mind of that generation." Even the great Einstein was influenced by music, "If I weren't a physicist, I'd probably be a musician. I often think in music, I live my daydreams in music, I see my life in terms of music."

What is it about music and sound that so greatly influences us?

Music has the power to change people. It affects not only how we think, but also:

- *physiologically*—our breathing, brain waves, heart rate

- *psychologically*—our emotions, instincts, motivation

- *behaviorally*—our embracing of pleasant sounds
  while avoiding unpleasant sounds.

One of the greatest sound bites in history is the famous *"Da-dun....*
Da-dun..." from the movie *Jaws*; it was the sound that always preceded the next shark attack. (If you slept through the 80's, or were waiting to be hatched, *Jaws* is a seminal movie featuring several frantic people fleeing a gigantic white shark that eats everything in its path.) In test audiences, the director found that the *"Da-dun....Da-dun..."* sound caused heart rates to

rise, signifying the onset of fear. After viewing the film, millions of people avoided the ocean in anything less than a WWII submarine.

The effects of music and sound are not restricted to movie-goers or even the human race. Animals, plants and inorganic objects are also effected by music and sound. The screech of a hovering hawk sends field mice scurrying for cover. Whales will gather around a sick whale and sing songs to help it recover. Certain musical notes have even been associated with helping plants grow to over twice their normal size—a process called *Sonic Bloom*. (Nope—I'm not making that up. Google it.) People, animals, plants—everything—is influenced by vibrational patterns.

We live in an ocean of motion. Everything in the universe is vibrating, from the smallest particles to the largest planets and stars. The chair you are sitting on is shaking ever so slightly. Every part of the chair—screws, fabric, wood, glue—are all humming at various frequencies. Even the walls are vibrating, especially if the teenage neighbor is into speed metal.

Strange as it might seem, we perceive the universe around us through vibrations. We hear, see, touch and smell by vibration. For example, we hear things because molecules are vibrating in patterns detected by the sensory receptors in our ears. Our ears are so sensitive that they can detect a change of less than one-billionth of atmospheric pressure, the force generated by air molecules transmitting vibrations to our ear drums (*Spectrums*, David Blatner, Bloomsbury, New York, 2012. pg 92).

We see because light frequencies are detected by the cones and rods of our eyes, sending messages to the brain that say, "There's a great white shark charging your small leaky boat." Vibrating light frequencies are the primary means by which cosmologists study the stars, planets and nebula of the universe.

Vibration is also how a chef cooks a gourmet meal, because heat is produced from vibrating light frequencies. In order to understand the universe around us, it is vital that we grasp the effects of vibrational frequencies. Let's start with examples of relatively large objects, as studied by classical physics.

Is it Live?... Or is it Memorex?

All matter has a resonant frequency—the frequency at which it will most readily vibrate and even amplify the stimulating energy. If you tap a wine glass, a particular tone will chime at the glass's resonant frequency. The Tacoma Narrows Bridge famously began vibrating violently under the influence of wind that stimulated the steel structure at its natural frequency. Resonant frequencies can be found in small objects such as kidney stones, which is how we blast them to smithereens rather than surgically remove them or pass them. Even Earth has a resonant frequency—it's somewhere between 6-10 hertz. (A hertz is a measure of oscillations per second). We can actually hear the resonant frequency of Earth, the other planets and the stars; recordings exist and are available on the internet.

Through a phenomenon called *mechanical resonance* (or *entrainment*), science has been able to use the resonant frequencies in objects for various purposes. Mechanical resonance occurs when a matching frequency comes into entrainment with an object's resonant frequency. If we take a wine glass and tap it with a spoon, it makes a particular sound. That is its resonant frequency. But if we were to sing at the glass at the same frequency, we would come into entrainment with the glass. With a sufficient amount of directed intensity, we would be able to stimulate the glass to the point where it shatters. (Just be sure to finish the wine first.)

What really happens when we shatter a glass? At the wine glass's molecular level, the additional intensity of the voice's matching frequency causes the glass molecules to vibrate more and more until they can no longer hold their form. The molecules eventually break apart, and we see the glass shearing apart. Of course, this is a case of accuracy over power. If you yelled at the top of your lungs but did not match the resonant frequency, entrainment would not be achieved and you would not be able to shatter the glass, only make yourself hoarse.

When I was a wee lad in the 70's, the Memorex company made their cassette tapes famous with a remarkable T.V. commercial. It featured the mechanical resonance of an opera singer shattering a wine glass with her voice. Then, in a show of their product's quality, another glass was shattered with a cassette recording of the singer. The company's tag line was: "Is it live? Or is it Memorex?" Of course, if it was the tape, it also meant they were also using an amplifier to create the sound, but who thought of such technicalities back then? It was an awesome commercial.

Does this Resonate with You?

There are many examples of mechanical resonance. As I said earlier, the medical profession uses mechanical resonance to break up kidney stones. By matching the frequency of a person's kidney stones, sonic frequencies are directed to the stones, causing them to break up as the molecules increase their vibration to the point where they can no longer hold their form.

The great scientist/inventor of the early 1900's, Nikola Tesla, inventor of Alternate Current (AC), also invented a mechanical resonance device. One day he tested it on a high rise building being constructed in Manhattan, NY, and discovered he could have leveled the building in a matter of minutes. The building steel was vibrating so violently, the steel workers fled in panic. He was so worried by its destructive power that he destroyed the machine. According to Tesla, through the phenomenon of mechanical resonance, if you had a large enough device, it would be possible to point the device at Earth and Earth would literally break apart. "If you want to find the secrets of the universe, think in terms of energy, frequency and vibration," said Nikola Tesla.

The principle of resonance illustrates that sound between two or more objects has a distinct relationship exclusive of other objects nearby—a form of entrainment. Objects can also come into entrainment with people. When a person sings, for example, they often come into entrainment with an accompanying guitar. However, an instrument will also come into entrainment with a singer. You can try this in the privacy of your own home. Hold a guitar 10 inches from your mouth and sing a note. Then stop singing and listen to the guitar. On its own, the guitar will be generating the same note you sang. Voila! The guitar has come into resonance with your voice.

The Power of Cymatics

As we learn some of the interesting phenomena of vibration, we can start to understand how much more is going on than is apparent to the casual observer. While previous chapters discussed how non-localized probability waves become our perceived reality, we have not addressed the mystery of how things in the universe obtain their shape. The best place for science to find answers to this quest is within the field of frequencies. Let's take a look at how frequencies can cause matter to come together and take form.

Cymatics comes from a Greek word meaning *waves*. It is the study of *modal vibration phenomena.* Big fancy term, eh? It's actually a much simpler concept than it sounds. By applying sound frequencies to matter, scientists have been able to discover interesting phenomenon occurring where matter comes together to take form.

A German physicist and musician, Ernst Florens Friedrich Chladni, first demonstrated how sound frequencies can manipulate sand to form beautiful symmetrical shapes. (See diagram 6.1). Known as the father of modern acoustics, Chladni developed a process where he applied frequencies to metal plates covered with sand. He found that different frequencies applied to the plate caused the sand to do different things— either be a shaking chaotic mess with no specific form, or make intricate geometric shapes on the metal plates. Vibrational node patterns formed on the metal plates when specific frequencies were applied to the plate.

Diagram 6.1 ~ I took these photos from one of my Chladni Plate demonstrations. Six separate shapes formed on plates by six different sound frequencies on a Chladni Plate.

In node areas where little or no vibration occurs, the sand collected and caused geometric shapes to form. As frequencies increased, the geometric shapes became more and more intricate.

The fundamental observation from these and other experiments is that different vibrational frequencies can cause matter to gather together in specific, orderly, geometric patterns.

Here is another example of how vibrating frequencies affect matter. I did an experiment involving cymatics on cooked rice. I had five different rice samples, each container consisting of rice and the water it was cooked in. To four of these containers, I applied four specific frequencies for 30 minutes per day. To the remaining fifth sample, I applied no frequencies.

The results were astonishing, although not very appetizing. First, the rice samples experiencing applied frequencies grew mold within a few days, while the control sample with no frequencies applied didn't grow mold until day eight. Second, the rice samples grew different color molds (green, rust, brownish/tan, white), depending on the frequency level applied. The results showed that vibrating frequencies affect how cooked rice reacts to the onset of mold. Not only did the different sound frequencies assist the onset of mold, they also determined which type of mold grew on the cooked rice.

Other, more famous experiments by Dr. Masaru Emoto have been conducted with water and sound frequencies. Dr. Emoto applied a variety of sounds to water samples to observe what would happen if the only variant in the experiment was the type of sound or frequency applied to the water. The results are stunning. Depending on the sound applied, the water molecules arranged themselves into a spectrum ranging from beautifully formed symmetric crystals to ugly deformed crystals. Some sounds formed intricately symmetric shapes, while other frequencies formed mutated or partially formed crystals.

Shake For Me

Cymatics is not restricted to sand on plates or molding rice. It gets way more interesting. Faraday waves are similar to vibrating modal nodes on a metal plate; however, they act as nonlinear standing waves within a liquid.

A fascinating example can be seen by applying varying frequencies through a function generator to a mixture of cornstarch and water—a viscous (thick, sticky), non-Newtonian fluid. The application of a single vibrating frequency will cause the mixture to form three-dimensional moving shapes (see diagram 6.2), not unlike the infamous blob that ate New Jersey.

People get blown away when I do this blob experiment (check out the video on my website) because they have no idea of the influence sound has on matter. The fact that a single frequency of sound will cause a fluid to rise up from a placid state to a three-dimensional moving blob sounds crazy until they actually see it.

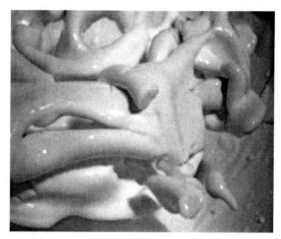

Diagram 6.2 ~ Non-Newtonian Fluid Cymatics.

Now consider this: If sound, as in this simple cymatics experiment, has an effect on matter to form new shapes, what effect does vibration have on other things?

- Rocks forming from molten lava?
- Solar systems forming from swirling dust clouds?
- A baby forming in the womb?
- A species forming under some process of evolution**?

** (Note: while I believe in evolution as a general adaptive nature of things—our Creator's means to allow species to adapt to the environment—I am not espousing a viewpoint of man descending from single-celled organisms, to the exclusion of intelligent design.)

Science is continuing to discover the implications of vibrating frequencies affecting matter, taking these experiments even further. Rather than applying sound and resurrecting a blob-like structure from cornstarch and water, scientists are learning they can actually control suspended objects in space and move them around simply by applying soundwaves to the object. Yoichi Ochiai, from the University of Tokyo, has done a number of experiments suspending and moving objects such as water droplets, screws and nuts. By adjusting the combination of sound waves, Ochiai is able to move the objects up, down, left and right without any physical contact. Cymatics research will continue to play an important role in discovering how atoms move and are attracted to each other through the influence of sound frequencies. (And for all we know, the blob is really out there, somewhere, biding its time.)

We'll Leave The Light On For You

Just as sound frequencies have an effect on matter, light frequencies also play a major role in the formation of things. We know about the electromagnetic radiation spectrum (EMR), consisting of light frequencies, including radio, infrared, microwave, visible, ultra-violet, x-ray and gamma waves. But do we realize how these frequencies change and form matter? Baking a cake at 400 degrees F uses light wave frequencies in the electromagnetic spectrum. The light frequencies affect the molecular structure of the cake as well as killing other molecular structures such as harmful bacteria. Most people don't put much thought into where heat actually comes from, they just like what it does.

For most of our everyday uses, light frequencies within the infrared and visible spectrum are the energy sources commonly used to effect changes in matter. The heat energy for cooking, sun tanning, hot showers, air conditioning and freezing, are all based on infrared frequencies. Yes, making ice involves heat. Compared to absolute zero (0° Kelvin, -459.67° Fahrenheit), ice cubes are really quite hot. In addition to heat, anything involving colors, such as clothing dye, art or house paint, uses frequencies within the visible light spectrum. Your blue jeans don't simply become blue because denim is blue. A specific dye is formulated so that when visible light is applied, certain light frequencies are absorbed by the fabric, and others are reflected. Guess which frequency is reflected. Yep! The blue light frequency.

Humans have become adept at manipulating light frequencies for our convenience. We understand that applying enough of the right EMR frequency can change liquid into a gas (water to vapor), solid matter into liquid (rock to magma), and liquid to solid (cake batter to cake).

What is not commonly understood, outside of the scientific community, is that these phenomena occur at the quantum level as well, down where the electrons and other subatomic particles live. If you recall the effects light has on electrons from Chapter 2 (quantum electrodynamics), congratulate yourself! You get an "A + + ." The important thing to remember is that everything is vibrating and light frequencies influence whatever matter does.

Chapter 2 discussed how, technically, electrons or atoms don't bond to other electrons or atoms; rather, they are bonded by light. We gave an analogy of a puzzle, and the atoms/electrons are the puzzle pieces trying to fit together with other atom/electrons, but light holds the puzzle pieces together so we can lift it off the table. The atoms that make up the molecules of a brick, for instance, are bonded together by electromagnetism. Light is what holds atoms together and prevents you from walking through a brick wall.

If it weren't for electromagnetism—a form of light—little would prevent you from walking through a wall. But then again, without electromagnetism, there would be no brick wall. The bricks would not exist because the atoms could not bond. The bottom line is this: Everything of substance is held together by light. If it weren't for light, there would be nothing—no stars, planets, people, books or bejeweled starlets shopping Rodeo Drive. Nothing. It is as though light is the universal glue.

Frontiers of Science

Through mechanical resonance and cymatics, we've briefly looked at how frequencies affect macro-atomic objects. And with our knowledge of quantum electrodynamics and the electromagnetic radiation spectrum (EMR), we know that frequencies have a powerful effect on subatomic particles. But science says there must be even more. While classical and quantum physics are discovering *what* is happening in the universe, they have problems understanding *how* and *why* these things are happening.

In the fervent search for greater truth, classical physics has uncovered, to date, 118 types of atoms—elements such as hydrogen, helium, carbon, oxygen and gold. These 118 atomic elements, alone or combining to form molecules, make up everything we know of in existence: rocks, water, stars, puppies, bananas and air. Everything.

Not to be outdone by classical physics, quantum physics has gone one step further and determined there are 12 fundamental building blocks of matter comprising all known subatomic particles: six types of quarks (*up, down, charm, strange, top, bottom*), plus six types of leptons (*electron, muon, tau, electron neutrino, muon neutrino, tau neutrino*). But most of these leptons and quarks exist outside our Earth's atmosphere. Of these 12 fundamental particles of matter, only three primarily exist on Earth and are needed to comprise any of the 118 elements. That's it: up quarks, down quarks and electrons. I'd venture to guess that less than 1 out of every 100,000 people realize that our bodies are made up of merely 3 different components of matter. You are now one of them. (You're going to sound pretty smart at the next family reunion)

In addition, there are five fundamental force-carrier particles called *bosons (photon, gluon, W boson, Z boson, Higgs Boson)* They are not particles of matter, but force carrier particles like electromagnetism, that act on the matter particles. Together, these make up the standard model of quantum physics.

I did not mention gravity and it's graviton particle; it is a separate force that is not included in the quantum standard model. Further, at the risk of getting confusing, I should mention that each of the six quarks and six leptons have an anti-matter particle, but these anti-matter particles are rare in our universe. If you recall in Chapter 2, anti-matter lost the battle during the inception of the big bang and was decimated.

Now, the description of quarks and leptons explains *what* is happening. We know the mass, spin and electric charge of these particles. But the deeper questions of *why* a particle has a certain amount of mass, and *why* are there only 17 fundamental particles (plus gravitons), and *how* a particle comes into existence, are the difficult areas science is painstakingly seeking to answer.

According to string physics, everything in the universe is made of the same thing—tiny vibrating strands of energy. As discussed in Chapter 1, physicists like to describe strings as something similar to a rubber band, flexible and able to stretch to different sizes. However, don't imagine that strings are literally a substance like a rubber band. Rather, think of the vibrations coming off a guitar string that make sound. Strings are vibrating forms of energy.

In Chapter 3, we covered the topic of quantum electrodynamics. This is where science discovered how electrons obtain and release energy through interacting with the electromagnetic force—photons, or light frequencies. Quantum physics looks at this process as wave frequencies and particles, while string physics looks at this process as the interaction between vibrating strands of energy. The point to understand is quantum science sees particles of atoms (quarks and leptons) and force particles (bosons) as two separate things, whereas string theorists see them all as the same thing, albeit playing different roles. String theory is not in opposition to the quantum perspective; rather, it builds upon and broadens the perspective of quantum physics.

Cosmic Symphony

Let's revisit the guitar analogy for a moment. As the guitar player plucks a string, it vibrates at a resonant pattern (see diagram 6.3). Of course, the standing strings on a guitar have many notes or resonant frequencies that can be played. The tiny strings of energy in the universe act in a similar way. Hypothetically, the universe has an infinite number of possible resonant frequencies. According to string theory, as a strand of energy vibrates, it creates a resonant pattern that determines which of the 17 + 1 known particles the string becomes—either one of the six quarks, six leptons or the 5 + 1 force particles. The frequency determines the particle type. Vary the frequency, vary the particle type.

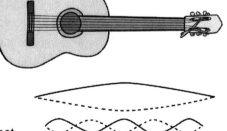

Einstein taught us that greater energy means greater mass. String theory claims the mass of an elementary particle (up quark, down quark, electron, etc.) is determined by the energy of its vibrational pattern. For example, consider the

Diagram 6.3 — Guitar strings vibrate resonant patterns similar to how strands of energy vibrate, determining what kind of subatomic particle it will be.

six types of quarks: *up, down, strange, charm, top* and *bottom.* An up quark has the least amount of mass, so it takes less energy to produce than a charm quark. The charm quark has less mass than the top quark, so it takes less energy to produce than the top quark.

The fundamental realization, according to string physics, is that everything—stars, planets, animals, people, subway trains, popcorn and popsicles—is composed from vibrations, a colossal cosmic symphony, the cacophony of creation.

Back to our guitar solo, consider that it doesn't take much for a person to pluck a guitar string and generate a particular note, especially if their name is Carlos Santana. A piano string, however, is much more difficult to pluck because of its high tension, which is why these strings are instead hammered.

The incredibly high tension of subatomic strings means the force necessary to generate a frequency that forms a particle is beyond our current capabilities. In fact, we may not soon attain the capability to control the energy needed to accomplish the task. However, this is not stopping physicists. The rewards of reaching this seemingly unattainable goal are enormous. For example, if physicists can produce the hardest particle to find—the graviton, which is the theoretical particle for gravity—all branches of physics would be changed forever.

But what a difficult task. According to string physics, the tension of a string is inversely proportional to the strength of the force transmitted. Because gravity is the weakest of the four forces—a million, billion, billion, billion, billion times weaker than the electromagnetic force—the proposed graviton particle would take the greatest amount of tension to produce. Calculations predict a needed thousand, billion, billion, billion, billion tons of Planck tension to produce a single graviton. For now, science must rely on the mathematics of string theory and search for gravitons in other ways.

String theory views the universe much differently than classical physics, which tends to see particles of atoms as hard substances akin to billiard balls on a pool table. While classical physics understands that particles are influenced by frequencies, it doesn't think of particles as being composed of vibrating strands of energy. As we said earlier, the vibrating frequency of each individual string determines its subatomic particle type: quark, lepton or zetting. (Just kidding—no one has named a particle after me... at least, not yet.) Because the vibrating frequencies of particles are affected by the frequencies of the four forces in nature—electromagnetism, strong nuclear, weak nuclear *and* gravity—science now has a viable explanation as to how particles are formed and why each has a consistent mass, spin and charge.

Let's put this into perspective. If quantum physics has determined that everything on Earth is comprised of up quarks, down quarks and electrons, then string theory declares that of the infinite number of possible frequencies that exist in the universe, only three frequencies are used. That's it—three. String theory indicates that up quarks are formed because of one particular frequency. No other frequency can create an up quark. Similarly, down quarks and electrons are also formed by specific frequencies. Which leads to the question: Why only three? (I've sat and pondered this incredible fact for days on end hoping my amazement of this important fact will rub off on you, my reader.)

Cell Adaptation

Because string theory deals with matter at the smallest, most fundamental level, it explores areas classical physics can't reach. Molecular biology can discover *what* is happening to a molecule, but has trouble with *how* or *why* it is happening. String theory tells us that the components of molecules are made of vibrating strands of energy, so anything occurring at the molecular level is a result of those vibrations.

The implications arising from string theory—that everything is made from vibrating frequencies of energy—need to be incorporated in our everyday worldview. Further, it is time to bring our earlier examples of cymatics into the conversation of strings. Certainly, through experiments with sand on Chladni Plates and non-Newtonian fluid forms, classical physics knows that frequencies affect matter. But to what degree is matter affected? Is there more going on that is forming the universe than meets the eye of classical physics? According to string theory, not only do vibrating frequencies form matter at the fundamental particle level, a cosmic symphony of frequencies helps to shape the universe.

We just finished describing how frequencies form the $17+1$ fundamental particles of the universe, including the three specific particles of matter that make up humans. So think of the up quarks, down quarks and electrons as the puzzle pieces from Chaper 3. Now let's bring in the frequencies that help to amass these fundamental particles into objects.

We would be remiss if we didn't bring up our friend, electromagnetism (light), since we have spent much time focusing on the importance light has from a quantum perspective on the formation and bonding of particles. The particle of electromagnetism is called a *photon*, and it is very different than the 12 building block particles of matter, primarily because photons do not have mass. Where up quarks, down quarks and electrons are limited to one, and only one, precise frequency, photons of light can exhibit an infinite number of frequencies as described within the electromagnetic radiation spectrum (EMR) (diagram 3.2). Throughout the universe, light has the unique ability to act within multiple frequencies. According to string theory, everything (galaxies, planets, trees, bacteria, viruses and even ice cream vendors) is formed by combinations of cosmic frequencies. This is the frontier of science and will affect the lives of countless future generations.

Here is a case in point. Science knows that the subcomponents of atoms are vibrating. All three branches of physics: classical, quantum and string, agree on this point. Everything is in constant motion: quarks, leptons, atoms, molecules, jello, planets and stars. Even you—my readers— are vibrating even as you consume these words. An average person is made of 200 trillion, trillion, trillion (2×10^{29}) vibrating fundamental particles that make up about 90 trillion (9×10^{10}) human and bacteria cells. Of these, you have some 25 trillion blood cells, and each second, roughly 2.5 million blood cells die and 2.5 million new cells grow.

Usually, a red blood cell reproduces and becomes another red blood cell; a bone cell reproduces into another bone cell and so forth. That makes sense, because things reproduce after their own kind, right? However, cells have a unique ability.

The most adaptable cells in the human body are called *stem cells*. They are unique because they are not specific to a type of cell; they are not muscle or blood or bone cells. They are located throughout the body and have the ability to become almost any cell type in your body. They are like a utility player in baseball who can play any position on the field: third base, shortstop, outfield or beer vendor. Because of this fantastic ability to become almost any type of cell, stem cells are highly sought after and cultivated by scientists for research.

Although biologists know that the environment of a stem cell plays a part in *why* a stem cell reproduces into a particular cell type, they don't know *how* a stem cell determines to become a particular cell type. The answers may very well lie with the frequency influences uncovered by string physics.

Consider what would happen if, instead of looking at muscle cells as individual cell entities, we viewed muscle cells as an environment influenced by combinations of frequencies, while blood and bone cells had their very own combination of environmental frequencies. Now science has a means to understand how stem cells become specific cells. Recall my rice experiment where different frequencies influenced the type of mold growing on the rice. Specific combinations of frequencies applied to stem cells could help determine if they become muscle cells, bone cells or any cell.

Why does light have the ability to incorporate infinite frequencies, while the three particles you and I are made up of are limited to exactly one frequency each? Further, if there are an infinite number of possible frequencies, why are there only 12 fundamental particles of matter (plus 12 anti-particles) that make up the entire universe, and not 1,926, or 265,198, or 247,347,767,989 fundamental particles? If random mutation is a fundamental belief in random evolution, then why don't we have mutations of the fundamental particles yielding new fundamental particles?

If random chance actually existed at the sub-atomic level, then within the billions of years since the big bang, it should have produced more—many more—fundamental particles. It hasn't. If stem cells can immediately become a muscle, blood or bone cell based on their environment, then why does evolution say it has to take millions of years for a species to evolve? According to string theory, there is no such requirement needed.

You have been presented with startling new information. For people who don't realize there are only 12 fundamental particles out of an infinite number of possibilities, there is reason—though based on unawareness—to assume everything in the universe is random. However, now that you know that string physics states there are only 12 defined frequencies for particles of matter, what do you do with this information?

Symphony Conductor

String theory offers the human race answers to the greatest and deepest questions about how the universe works. Just as Isaac Newton turned the attention of the world to science in the late 1600's, string physics has the potential to uncover as many or more mysteries of the universe as Newton's classical physics. Of course, exploring string theory will take decades, perhaps centuries. In its favor, however, mathematics supports string theory, and it is the only theory that successfully connects the four forces of the universe: electromagnetism, strong nuclear, weak nuclear and gravity. At the very least, string theory forces us to expand beliefs beyond the falsehood that reality is only what we see, touch, hear, smell and taste.

To illustrate the ideas behind string theory, physicists often use musical instruments, such as a French horn, guitar or piano to demonstrate how vibrating strings of energy work. The vibrating energy of a unique note illustrates how a unique string vibration forms a unique subatomic particle —one of the $17 + 1$. Of course, put enough of these notes together and you have a musical score.

String theory's 18 fundamental frequencies of energy, producing the 18 fundamental particles of the subatomic world, combine to form the musical score of our existence. Everything we know is formed by the melodic intertwining of these instruments—a symphony of the universe. Think of yourself as a song. But like any instrument, to produce a note, the instrument must somehow be played. In other words, if there is a piano note, there must be a pianist. And if there is a Hotel California, there must be the Eagles.

Which leads us to the next question: How is the symphony of the universe being composed? Who holds the baton? Is it human consciousness or a universal consciousness? Is it God? Or some sub-being acting as an intelligent designer? A French horn sitting on the ground does not play on its own; a musician plays the notes. Likewise, different frequencies cause different particles to form, but the question remains: Who or what causes the specific vibrations to occur?

It is unlikely that string physicists intend the analogy of musical instruments to lead us to conclude that a cosmic conductor or intelligent life is involved, but that is exactly where these examples lead us. Musical instruments imply the existence of a player that plays the notes. I've racked my brain for another analogy that does not lead to this conclusion. I can't think of one.

Word

Science didn't have to ask these questions 100 years ago because they didn't know to ask. However, now that science is discovering the bizarre ways in which the universe works, we have to incorporate these questions into our worldview. To do so, we must develop a healthy appetite for the abstract, the ambiguous, the "yet to be defined" areas at the frontiers of our fledgling knowledge. We can't ignore what science is uncovering in order to protect the beliefs feeding our sense of security derived from the illusion of having everything figured out. All beliefs, theories and suppositions need to be open for discussion.

Since our study is focused on how science supports the possibility that the universe was created and is sustained by a creator God, let's review what the Bible conveys regarding vibrations.

If the universe is a symphony, is God the conductor? Put another way, does God lead the instruments in the necessary frequencies to produce the 18 fundamental particles comprising the universe? Is it possible that God can bring matter together into form and hold things together over time? Is it possible that God is the musician that plays the specific frequencies of the subatomic particles that produced the protocell, or the frequencies of the Aspergillus Niger Fungi, or the specific frequencies for a dog?

As we learned, the Bible clearly describes God as light. It is God's essence and one of the ways He is present throughout the universe, both in the invisible, non-local realm and in the visible, localized realm. In addition, much of what the Bible says about frequencies has already been brought up in the earlier chapters on quantum electrodynamics (demonstrating

God's omnipresence), and light frequencies within the electromagnetic radiation (EMR) spectrum. These earlier references, however, discussed the relationship of light frequencies to particular phenomena that occur in the quantum world, such as omnipresence and transitioning from the non-local invisible realm into the localized visible realm, and how the God of Light correlates to these phenomena. Here we are discussing God's relevance in the form of light frequencies and how these frequencies affect form and function.

As we discuss light and the electromagnetic force, it is important to remember that atoms bond to each other and maintain their structure. A water molecule is written as "H_2O" because it is made of two hydrogen atoms and one oxygen atom, forming a bond between the three atoms. The term *bond* becomes confusing, though, because we may think it is the atoms that bond together. It's not like that at the atomic level. The water molecule is like a puzzle of two hydrogen pieces and one oxygen piece fitted together. If you try and pick up a puzzle from your kitchen table, it falls to pieces. It is light that bonds the atoms together so they don't fall apart. Light is required to hold all objects in place.

Keep in mind that physics claims the 12 building block particles of matter are restricted to a single frequency each, while light has the freedom to have an infinite number of frequencies in play. This freedom of frequency range allows light to be instrumental in the composition and function of objects. Light is essential in the composition of molecules such as the H_2O molecule, for example. And it facilitates the functional qualities of things like a "hard" brick, a "cooked" chicken or a "red" rose. Is it a coincidence that particles of light are so different from particles of matter? It is astounding that the Bible isolates the one substance we know of in the universe that can form objects and hold them together. Here again are some Bible verses describing God as light.

> *As the appearance of the rainbow in the clouds on a rainy day, so was the appearance of the surrounding radiance. Such was the appearance of the likeness of the glory of the LORD. And when I saw it, I fell on my face and heard a voice speaking.*
>
> *Ezekiel 1:28*

> *Then Jesus again spoke to them, saying, "I am the Light of the world; he who follows Me will not walk in the darkness, but will have the Light of life."*
>
> *John 8:12*

> *And He was transfigured before them; and His face shone like the sun, and His garments became as white as light.*
>
> *Matthew 17:2*

> *At midday, O King, I saw on the way a light from heaven, brighter than the sun, shining all around me and those who were journeying with me.*
>
> *Acts 26:13*

> *And He is the radiance of His glory and the exact representation of His nature, and upholds all things by the word of His power...*
>
> *Hebrews 1:3*

> *And the city has no need of the sun or of the moon to shine on it, for the glory of God has illumined it, and its lamp is the Lamb.*
>
> *Revelation 21:23*

Physics knows that everything in the universe is vibrating, and like the Chladni plate example, vibrations can cause matter to form into exquisite formations. But Chladni configurations pale in comparison to what string theory says occurs through vibrations: stars, planets and life itself are formed by vibrating strings. Let's take a look at some of the verses written in the Bible that refer to God's breath and voice, and see how they describe the creation and sustaining of the universe.

The Hebrew word *dabar* generally means *word*, but it also includes *utterance* in the sense of not being of a particular language. Further, the Greek term for *word*, which is *logos*, embodies *a concept, an idea, a decree, a mandate, or an order of moral precepts given by God*. Just as the definition for *utterance* is not tied to a specific language, scriptures using terms such as *voice, words, says and commanded,* don't necessarily mean that God is speaking in Hebrew, Arabic, Greek, Latin or English. Instead, these terms can refer to sounds and utterances consisting of particular vibrational patterns and frequencies. Just as a guitar or bassoon doesn't speak Russian or Pidgin, so also God's utterances in their purest form are not specific to language as we know it.

With that understanding, let's take a look at some of the verses written in the Bible that refer to God's breath and voice, and see how they describe creating and sustaining the universe.

> *In the beginning was the Word, and the Word was with God, and the Word was God. He [Christ Jesus] was in the beginning with God. All things came into being through Him, and apart from Him nothing came into being that has come into being.*
>
> *John 1:1-3*

> *"So will My word be which goes forth from My mouth; It will not return to Me empty, without accomplishing what I desire, and without succeeding in the matter for which I sent it."*
>
> *Isaiah 55:11*

> *The voice of the* LORD *is upon the waters; the God of glory thunders, the* LORD *is over many waters. The voice of the* LORD *is powerful; the voice of the* LORD *is majestic.*
>
> *Psalm 29:3-4*

> *By faith we understand that the worlds were prepared by the word of God, so that what is seen was not made out of things which are visible.*
>
> *Hebrews 11:3*

> *By the word of the* LORD *the heavens were made, and by the breath of His mouth all their host. He gathers the waters of the sea together as a heap; He lays up the deeps in storehouses. Let all the earth fear the* LORD; *let all the inhabitants of the*

*world stand in awe of Him. For He spoke, and it was done; He
commanded, and it stood fast.*

Psalm 33:6-9

*And He Himself existed and is before all things, and in
Him all things hold together. [He is the controlling, cohesive
force of the universe.]*

Colossians 1:17 amplified

*"After it, a voice roars; He thunders with His majestic
voice, and He does not restrain the lightnings when His voice
is heard. God thunders with His voice wondrously, doing great
things which we cannot comprehend. For to the snow He says,
'Fall in the earth,' And to the downpour and the rain, 'Be strong.'*

Job 37:4-6

Old Habits Die Hard

When you read in Genesis of the heavens being made, or in Job about snow falling on the Earth, do these verses ever seem silly? I mean, everyone knows that snow falls because water vapor freezes, accumulates into clouds to a point where the atmospheric pressure cannot sustain the weight of the water vapor any longer, and then gravity causes the water to fall. Then, if the atmospheric temperature is too cold for the vapor to form liquid water molecules, the water vapor molecules become snow.

From a classical physics perspective, this explanation is correct. However, we must remember there are three branches of physics that have a say in what happens when snow falls. In today's world, classical physics has only one perspective and it is not inclusive to the other two realities of quantum and string physics. As modern people, we need a broader physics understanding of the world, otherwise we limit our awareness of the reality we inhabit.

From a string physics perspective, snow falls because of vibrational patterns. The water molecules, the temperature, the force of gravity, are all the result of vibrating frequencies. Change the vibrational frequency of the temperature, and rain falls instead of snow. And because physics is neutral to the concept of God, string physics does not say that vibrational patterns can't come from a God source.

So, how much does vibration and sound have to do with the formation of the universe? Consider this scientific perspective about sound, by David Blatner.

> *Sound is ultimately absorbed and converted into heat. And scientists estimate that these tones, these rich, vast roars, provide as much energy throughout the galaxy as billions of suns. It's as though the music of the spheres, heating this interstellar gas, helps create just the right conditions for new stars and galaxies to be born.*

Spectrums, David Blatner, pg. 103

Doesn't this seem like a scripture verse sans a reference to God?

God is Viable

The Bible describes God as not only the initial creator, but one who is active throughout time. God did not create and run. He did not intend creation to continue without his involvement. This is a good thing for creationists because if God is to remain consistent with the requirements of physics, God would have to be active from the beginning, through the present and into the future. As physics examines how the universe works, we learn that light and vibrating frequencies occur as much today as 4.5 billion years ago when Earth formed, signifying God's constant involvement.

Recall our previous discussion about 12 fundamental subatomic particles of matter available in the universe. Intelligent design—the argument for the existence of a creator—addresses the issue of these 12 specific particles rather neatly. From the infinite possibilities of vibrations creating particles, only 12 fundamental particles of matter exist in our reality. Not 1,785, not 3,287 and not 29,865,999. Twelve.

God has the ability to choose the 12 frequencies required to produce these fundamental particles of the universe. I realize this is a simplistic answer, but it is much better than saying, "It is so, because God is big." It is a better answer because science has laid down extremely specific requirements and the God of the Bible clearly matches the requirements;

astonishingly, from oral traditions and written transcripts thousands of years prior to any knowledge of quantum or string physics.

Apart from proving atheism is not a feasible idea, our study is not about debunking other theories and beliefs. It is about presenting scientific phenomena occurring in the universe and understanding how the God described in the Bible lines up with these phenomena through extraordinary parallels. We are demonstrating that science supports the possibility that God exists. In fact, science says the universe acts more like what is written in the Bible than what is written in a high-school science book.

So far we have discussed how vibrating strands of energy manifest in our four-dimensional realty. Could more be happening around us than we can see, touch and hear? We already know from quantum physics that everything in the localized visible world transitions from an unseen non-local realm. We are about to learn that science claims there are more dimensions than the four we experience on a day to day basis.

Chapter 7

~~~~~~

Additional Dimensions

This Universe Goes To Eleven

Scientists studying the world around us have so far proven there are three spatial dimensions that encompass space. These three dimensions are commonly referred to as width, height and depth. Physicists, including Einstein, have been working on various theories involving additional dimensions for the past century.

The concept of a fourth spatial dimension was first introduced mathematically in 1919 by the German mathematician Theodor Kaluza and the Swedish physicist Oskar Klein. The concept proved to be ahead of its time. One of the amazing features of the Kaluza-Klein equations was that they unified Einstein's theory of gravity with Maxwell's theory of light. In the physics world, this was a major accomplishment. No other mathematically-based theory had yet accomplished this feat. But the theory had some problems to overcome, which caused the study of extra dimensions to lose interest among the scientific community. It took physics some 60 years to catch up to the ideas of Kauza-Klein.

The idea of extra spatial dimensions was revived in the 70's and 80's through string theory (M theory). In order for string theory to unify the four forces of nature (electromagnetism, strong nuclear, weak nuclear and gravity), there has to be additional spatial dimensions. According to string theory, this is non-negotiable; there MUST be extra dimensions! And not just one additional dimension as Kaluza-Klein proposed. It took until the mid-1990's to zero in on the exact number of dimensions, but string physicists now say there must be at least 7 additional dimensions for a total of 11 (10 spatial dimensions plus 1 spacetime dimension).

The concept of extra dimensions is so extreme, it took the scientific community many years to accept the idea, and even today, there are holdout scientists who doubt the existence of additional dimensions. However, string theory is the only viable theory that unifies General Relativity and quantum mechanics. The most accurate mathematical equations and best path to uncover the fascinating mysteries of the universe lie within string theory (M-theory).

(Note: I include M-theory because it has some additional aspects to standard string theory that are important for the accuracy of my statements.)

The Stakes are High

Trying to describe additional dimensions is a daunting task, nearly as difficult as discovering them in the first place. How does one communicate something when no one knows what it looks like or how it works? No one can observe, measure, or show a cause/effect process of extra dimensions. So at present, they are un-verifiable, known only as theoretical issues without proof of how they operate. Physicists are therefore reduced to describing additional dimensions with creative illustrations, waving their arms madly through the air while grasping for verbiage yet invented.

Consider the plight of science. On the one hand, it is extremely frustrating searching for something you don't know exists or even can be found. On the other hand, it is one of richest scientific frontiers ever explored. Physics is on a priceless treasure hunt. The stakes are astonishing, the potential is staggering, and success portends the reality of dreams such as time travel, intra-galactic navigation and children obeying parents. (Sorry, I got carried away there. What was I thinking?) For now, science must rely on a map and clues luring them far beyond our three-dimensional universe. Yet, the scientists who uncover the secrets of extra dimensions will be forever heralded as the greatest minds in history.

Some Basics

On the surface, dimensions seem fairly easy to understand. There is width, height and depth (or thickness). Dimensions are a great way to communicate size and location through right/left (width), up/down (height) forward/backward (depth) coordinates. These are what are called the *three spatial dimensions* because they occupy space. (Spatial = space.) However, the dynamics of dimensions can get confusing, especially when we get into additional dimensions, so I'll try to keep it simple. For our discussion, we will not consider time, which is referred to as the *fourth dimension*. It is a different animal, and we will deal with it in the next chapter.

Before we address extra spatial dimensions, however, let's discuss the three dimensions we are familiar with and highlight some of their peculiarities. We'll start by defining the zero-th (0th) dimension.

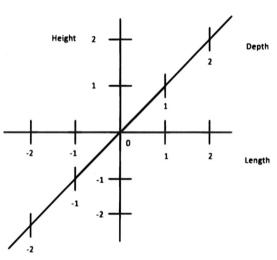

In diagram 7.1 we have spatial lines that represent length, height and depth. Because dimensions describe the occupation of space, a single point in space presents interesting issues. Technically, it doesn't need any of the three coordinates (left/ right, up/down, forward/ backward) to describe it. Think about it: How high is a point? How thick? Diagram 7.1 ~ Intersection of length, height, depth is at zero.

Therefore, a point is referred to as a zero-dimensional object. The point exists in space; it just happens to have zero as a value.

A line, on the other hand, moves in one direction at a time, either right/left, up/down or forward/backward. But it can't do all three; in fact, it can't even do two, because that would be two dimensions. A line can only inhabit one dimension, even if the line is curved (diagram 7.2). A curved line is considered one-dimensional because you can only move along the line. Don't be confused thinking that a line moving forward/backward would be operating in two or three dimensions. Each dimension needs to be thought of as its own entity. In other words, it doesn't matter if a line is moving left/right, up/down or forward/backward, each is relatively the same thing; you can only move along the line in one direction, i.e. left/right OR up/down.

Diagram 7.2 — Lines are formed by connecting multiple points. The size and/or location of a line is described by using the coordinates of one dimension of either right/left (width), up/down (height) or forward/backward (depth). Even a curved line acts in one dimension.

Now, if we were to add a second line that intersected the first line, we would move into two dimensions (diagram 7.3). These two lines would operate in two dimensions because it takes two directional coordinates to describe the size and/or location of the lines, i.e. left/right *and* up/down. Next, let's arrange the lines into a rectangle. We are still in two dimensions because it still takes only two coordinates to describe the rectangle's size and location.

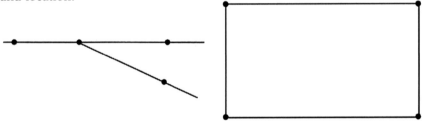

Diagram 7.3 The size and/or location of two intersecting lines and a rectangle are both examples of two dimensions because they are described by using the coordinates of two dimensions, such as, right/left (width) and up/down (height).

A cube, on the other hand, uses all three spatial dimensions and therefore is three-dimensional (diagram 7.4). If you wanted to locate a point within a cube, you would need three coordinates to describe it—left/right, up/down and forward/backward. (In math, we refer to these as x, y and z coordinates on a three-dimensional grid.) So considering the extremes of the three-dimensional spatial world, the point is zero-dimensional while the cube is three-dimensional. So far, so good.

An important concept to remember is that the third dimension is dependent upon the other two dimensions being present. Depth as the third dimension needs to have the other dimensions of length and height present as well. The same goes for two dimensions. Two dimensions can't be present without the first dimension present. Height (Up/down) for example, can't operate as the second dimension without length (left/right) being present.

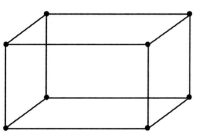

Diagram 7.4   The size and/or location of a cube is described by using the coordinates of all three dimensions, right/left (width), up/down (height) and forward/backward (depth) and therefore is a three-dimensional object.

Of course, these are different explanations for something we already know intuitively. We exist in a three-dimensional world, hence we accept it without thinking too hard about it. Sometimes, science can confuse things by describing common everyday qualities in language that seems needlessly complicated. The goal is not confusion, however, nor is it to show how smart scientists can be. It is instead to get us thinking in scientific terms so that additional concepts can be introduced with the same scientific viewpoint—concepts we haven't yet considered. Before science can teach us something new, it must establish a framework through which new ideas can flow.

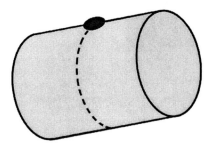

Diagram 7.5 ~ An ant walking on the surface of a cylinder only needs two-dimensional coordinates (left/right and up/down) to describe its position, therefore, a three-dimensional object can be perceived as a two-dimensional surface. If the ant burrows into the cylinder, it would need three-dimensional coordinates to locate its position.

Working with dimensional objects and describing additional dimensions can get a little tricky, which is why we first made the effort to describe three-dimensional objects. For example, take a cylinder (diagram 7.5). If an ant were to walk around the surface of the cylinder, technically, you would only need two coordinates to locate its position (i.e. left/right and up/down). In this scenario, you are describing the ant on a two-dimensional plane. But if the ant were to burrow into the cylinder, you would then need three coordinates to describe the ant's position in three dimensions.

Fourth Spatial Dimension

So what does the fourth *spatial* dimension look like? (Not to be confused with the fourth dimension of time or spacetime, which will be discussed in the next chapter.) To get an idea of the fourth *spatial* dimension, let's review the process of the first few dimensions and work our way up to it. We started with a zero-th dimension—a point. Now, if you want to make a line—a one-dimensional object—you connect at least two points together (diagram 7.6). In other words, a one-dimensional line is made up of a collection of connected zero-dimensional points. (At least two dots for a straight line; more for a curved line). This process of connecting points continues to form each successive dimension. A collection of connected lines makes a two-dimensional plane (diagram 7.7). A collection of connected planes forms a three-dimensional cube (diagram 7.8).

Diagram 7.6 ~ Connected dots form a one-dimensional line

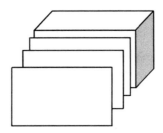

Diagram 7.7 ~ Parallel lines can connect to form a two-dimensional plane

Diagram 7.8 ~ Parallel planes can connect to form a three-dimensional cube

Finally, adding a collection of connected cubes forms a four-dimensional geometric shape called a *tesseract* (diagram 7.9). Yeah, I bet you were with me until *tesseract*. Don't feel bad. A tesseract is a four-dimensional analog of the cube. It is to the cube what a cube is to the plane.

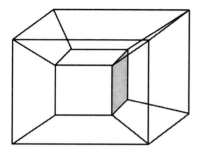

Diagram 7.9 ~ Parallel cubes can connect to form a fourth spatial dimensional tesseract

Nobody's seen a tesseract, not really. As humans, we don't see things in the fourth spatial dimension. Three dimensions (plus time) is our perceptual limit. Therefore, it gets very interesting trying to figure out what four spatial dimensions would be like. We don't really know what it would be like with a fourth spatial dimension. We are like goldfish stuck in a glass bowl trying to understand the living room. Okay, we are a little smarter than goldfish, so we can at least make some educated guesses.

Dot Dot Dash

Just as there is no limit to the number of points that can be connected to form lines, there is no limit to the number of lines to form planes, nor planes to form cubes, nor cubes to form tesseracts. Considering these possibilities, the universe becomes more diverse than we ever thought possible.

But why should the universe seem so strange? The points, lines, planes and cubes are recognizable objects for us to identify and give meaning to the different dimensions. We use these objects to describe what we see; they represent our universe. For example, the cube (or it's more liberal cousin, the sphere), can represent the entire universe within three dimensions. According to this model, all the stars, planets, nebulae and empty space are in this cube. We just need a really big cube.

When we add the fourth spatial dimension to a cube, a tesseract is formed. A tesseract, as we said earlier, is an analog way to describe the fourth spatial dimension. Where a cube consists of 6 faces (think of a dice with numbers 1 thru 6), plus 12 edges and 8 vertices, a tesseract consists of

8 cells, 24 faces, 32 edges and 16 vertices. It's a cube on steroids. A super-cube! The Cube of cubes!!

Now let's talk about perspective. Theoretically, the fourth spatial dimension would be able to see the entirety of the other three dimensions. If you were to look at your neighbor's house, you would only see the front of the house. From four dimensions you would be able to see the house from every angle. It would be as though you had eyes looking from the front, both sides, the back and from above, all at the same time.

The Red Pill Or The Blue Pill

The Matrix is a blockbuster movie from 1999, in which the characters exist in two realities. One reality is the two-dimensional world generated by a computer program that mimicked the 3-D world we all know and love, while the other reality is the true, dystopian three-dimensional world that constitutes actual reality—a reality unknown to those deceived by the computer program. The characters in the true three-dimensional world are trying to liberate those held in bondage by computers within the two-dimensional world. Those stuck in the two dimensions believe they existed in reality and are unaware of the truth that there is more to reality than they can imagine. The only way to liberate the people in the two-dimensional world is for the people in three dimensions to transition to two dimensions and rescue them.

Quantum and string physics are telling us that our existence is similar to that of the movie characters; there is more than what we see, hear, touch and taste. We think that we live in a real world of three dimensions (plus time), while science is moving towards the realization that we actually exist in more dimensions.

> *You take the blue pill—the story ends, you wake up in your bed and believe whatever you want to believe. You take the red pill—you stay in Wonderland and I show you how deep the rabbit-hole goes.*
>
> Morpheus, in *The Matrix*, Wachowski, Warner Bros. 1999

Flatville

In everyday life, people don't have a problem understanding the three spatial dimensions of height, width and depth. After all, that is how we perceive the world around us. However, getting into conceptual ideas of points, lines, planes, cubes and tesseracts can blast us from our comfort zone at warp speed. And since we don't perceive more dimensions, it can be difficult to grasp the idea of additional dimensions beyond our cherished three.

An easy way to start understanding extra dimensions is to first think of what the world would be like if it existed in just two dimensions. We'll call it Flatville (taken from the concept from Edwin Abbott's *Flatland*, Princeton: Princeton University Press, 1991). The town of Flatville exists on a two-dimensional surface, or as physicists like to call it—a brane (as in *membrane*). Think of the brane as a sheet of paper (see diagram 7.10).

Diagram 7.10 ~ Suzy and John of Flatville exist on a 2 dimensional plane

Flatville is a small town of only two people: Suzy and John. They exist as two cut-out paper dolls lying on top of the paper surface. (For my perfectionist readers, yes, technically, paper dolls have the depth of paper. For our illustration, the good people of Flatville have no depth.)

When John looks over at Suzy, he sees Suzy as a line. This is because they can only see along the two-dimensional plane. They can't look up or down, because to them, *up* and *down* don't exist. At least in their immediate world of limited perception, they don't exist…even though *up* and *down* do exist to beings living in the three-dimensional world.

When John moves around Suzy, he can see that Suzy has an outer shape. They can understand that each is comprised of two coordinates: width and height (not to be confused with depth). John and Suzy experience their world as two dimensions. Being stuck on the two-dimensional plane means they don't have the ability of the third dimension to perceive the coordinates of depth. They have no idea what the third dimension is. Because of this, John can't see that Suzy is wearing a polka dot dress. So even though they have their outlines, no one in Flatville knows what it looks like on the inside. They can't see past the line in their immediate line of sight.

In order for John to see Suzy's dress, he would need to have the third dimension of depth to see from above. As you look at diagram 7.11, we see Suzy is wearing a polka dot dress, we see this because we are looking down at Flatville from above. John and Suzy don't have the dimensional advantage you and I have looking at Flatville from three dimensions. Our three-dimensional perspective allows us to understand there is more to the people of Flatville than they can perceive.

Diagram 7.11 ~ John and Suzy of Flatville are on a 2-dimensional membrane. John only sees Suzy as a line. Since we are in three dimensions, we can see John and Suzy from the additional dimension of depth.

Now let's have some fun. We'll move some three-dimensional cubes through the two-dimensional brane (see diagram 7.12) into John and Suzy's world. As the cubes pass through the two-dimensional membrane, they exist above the plane, on the plane and below the plane. But from the perspective of John and Suzy, the cubes are seen as lines. They have no idea the cubes exist. Only the portion of the cube that splices through the brane can be perceived by the people of Flatville. From our perspective in three dimensions, we perceive the cubes as cubes (3-D) and squares (2-D). At this point, Suzy is wondering why John can't be more like a cube and less like a square, but that's just her intuition. She really has no idea what a cube is.

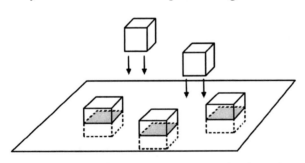

Diagram 7.12 ~ 3-dimensional cubes passing through a 2-dimensional membrane. The people of Flatville will only see lines where the cubes interact with the 2-dimensional membrane.

Here's the problem. Since Suzy and John are restricted to the surface of two dimensions, they have difficulty understanding that more is going on in the universe than they can perceive. They find themselves facing the same dilemma that physics faces today. We are stuck on the surface of three dimensions, knowing that more is going on in additional dimensions. We have to find ways to get off the three-dimensional surface so we can prove there is more. This is one reason why physics is so exciting. It reaches beyond the conventional limits.

Polka Dot Dress?

What if we went to Flatville and told Suzy and John about additional dimensions, also mentioning that Suzy wears a polka dot dress? Because we still exist in three dimensions however, just like the cube, only the portion of us that splices through the membrane appears to John and Suzy (diagram 7.13). When they look at us, they see us as a line making the

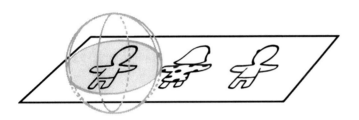

Diagram 7.13 ~ If we existed in extra dimensions and part of us split the plane of Flatville we would still exist in extra dimensions outside the plane of Flatville, but the people of Flatville could only see our two-dimensional outer shape as a line.

outline of a shape, just like they are. We appear to look like them. They have no idea that part of us is hovering just above their world.

It gets better. When we (science) tell Suzy she is wearing a polka dot dress, she thinks we are crazy. She has no grid to understand what we are talking about. Discussions about a third dimension that allows us to see Suzy's dress from above don't make any sense to her. The concept of *above* is weird. We can't draw a picture of the dress because they don't have a way to see the drawing.

While we have the ability to introduce new concepts to John and Suzy, it is frustratingly difficult, not to mention dangerous. For example, they don't have any way to write or collect data—that requires three dimensions, so it is difficult to teach things like mathematics. John and Suzy are restricted to the knowledge and physical laws of their two-dimensional world, so we have to come up with creative ways to educate them. We discover that analogies and metaphors help us make progress. In the end, we leave John and Suzy without absolute proof of the third dimension, let alone what a polka dot dress is, but they have to wonder what happened to us, how we appeared, spoke some incomprehensible nonsense and just as suddenly disappeared. We, on the other hand, leave hoping we have given Suzy and John enough insight for them to someday prove things on their own within the restrictions of Flatville. Meanwhile, Suzy starts to wonder about polka dot dresses.

Are We Flatville?

Now imagine humans are the people of Flatville, although, instead of existing on a two-dimensional membrane surface, we exist on a three-dimensional membrane. Next, imagine there is something in four or five spatial dimensions looking at us just as we observed John and Suzy. What would we look like from their perspective? What could they see about us that we can't? What are our polka dot dresses? Am I wearing a dress and I don't even know it? (Perish the thought!) What would their multi-dimensional universe be like, and how would ours appear to them?

Some people think that what they see, touch, hear and taste around them is everything; just like the people of Flatville believe everything is just lines. According to string physics, that is a very simplistic and safe view of our world. But never content to leave things as they are, science says that other dimensions must exist outside our three dimensions. The physicists that study string physics and additional dimensions know they are on the most difficult journey mankind has ever tackled. Armed with not much more than mathematics and the desire to know the truth, they are determined to go where no man has gone before. And yes, some are wearing dresses.

Think Inside the Box™

The use of Flatville is an excellent way for people to begin to grasp the concept of extra dimensions. M-theorists (a branch of string theory) are optimistic they will someday discover dimensions other than our three.

Some people even have the notion that these extra dimensions exist outside our observable universe in a way which engulfs our dimensions, as in diagram 7.13.

Mathematics also leads string physics to an alternative location. You have heard the term, *think outside the box,* well, it's time to *think inside the box.*™ A probable place for these extra dimensions to exist is where Kaluza and Klein predicted back in 1919—very tiny dimensions curled up inside the three dimensions of height, width and depth.

Picture two skyscrapers with a wire strung between them. As you look up, a tightrope walker starts walking across on the wire. From the ground, the thin wire appears to be a one-dimensional line. As far as we're concerned, the tightrope walker is going in one dimension from building to building—right to left—along the wire.

Now we decide to take a closer look with our binoculars. To our surprise, we see an ant walking in front of the tightrope walker, about to be stepped on. To avoid this fate, the ant rotates axially to the underside of the wire and continues walking building to building in the same direction as the tightrope walker. The ant has used the advantage of two dimensions on the wire's surface to escape being squished to death. If the ant were able to burrow into the middle of the wire, it would have been able to use three dimensions—even better! But since the ant isn't able to penetrate the steel wire, it's a good thing it only needed two dimensions to elude the tightrope walker's foot.

Extra dimensions are like the wire illustration. The wire first appeared to be one-dimensional. Looking more closely however, we discovered that it had two dimensions, and then a total of three dimensions. String physicists propose that the three-dimensional world we see around us may actually have more dimensions if we look closer. Imagine the wire being so tiny that we could not see it even with the most technically advanced equipment. It is so small that the contents inside the wire cannot be detected from our three-dimensional universe. So the wire exists, yet we can't observe it from the constraints of our three-dimensional perspective. Mathematically it is there, but practically it is undetectable.

We had always thought there were only three dimensions in our universe because we could scientifically observe them. However, according to string physics, there lies within our midst the likelihood of additional dimensions so small we cannot detect them.

The Calabi-Yau

The Kaluza-Klein theory brought forth the concept of one additional dimension, but string theory (M-theory) demands seven additional dimensions. Imagining even one additional dimension was difficult, for even the likes of Einstein to comprehend, but seven additional dimensions? Isn't this getting out of hand? Hey, I'm just the messenger. As odd as it sounds, there isn't anything known to science that rejects the possibility for multiple dimensions to exist.

Piggy-backing on the concept of the Kaluza-Klein theory is the concept of multiple dimensions curled up within each other, called *Calabi-Yau* spaces. Instead of one additional curled up dimension, Calabi-Yau spaces mathematically propose a way for six additional curled dimensions to exist. Of course, it's especially difficult to explain what a Calabi-Yau shape looks like (see diagram 7.14). When I speak to groups, I like to use a poofy shower sponge as a visual example of a Calabi-Yau manifold. A shower pouf is a mesh substance tied up in a way that produces lots of folds and undulations.

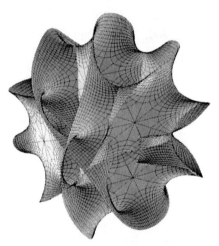

Diagram 7.14 ~ Example of a six-dimensional Calabi-Yau space (manifold). Depending where the string is located within the space determines which extra dimension it is in.

Mathematically, Calabi-Yau spaces must meet very stringent guidelines for a specific model to qualify, so my shower pouf example is a loose representation. In any event, if you have ever seen a shower pouf, you can get a pretty good idea of what a Calabi-Yau manifold concept looks like. In these Calabi-Yau spaces, particles and force charges exist dependent upon the specific vibrating frequency producing them. Depending on where the vibrating string of energy is within the Calabi-Yau space determines which extra dimension the string is located. Theoretically, at every point in three-dimensional space, there are six additional curled-up dimensions. Inside each curled dimension lies a one-dimensional string.

Maybe Horton Really Did Hear A Who

Take a moment to consider the ramifications of these additional dimensions. Who are we? Is there more to our existence than we thought? Science says these tiny curled up folds of dimensions could exist at every point in space, from the farthest reaches of the universe to the planet Earth. Does this mean they exist in you and me?

Look at your hand for a moment. You see skin as it covers the bones, ligaments, muscles and veins. Now imagine there is more going on inside your hand, because at every point of space, there could exist additional dimensions. Hypothetically, you don't consist of just three dimensions, but possibly four, five, six or more. There is literally more to you than meets the eye.

Of course, not everyone reacts well to the idea of added dimensions. Some people don't care that they are more than what biology teaches. Still, in light of recent discoveries, it is becoming increasingly difficult to believe the world we see, touch, hear and taste is everything, unless we can ignore science.

Others however, are fascinated with the possibilities of who they are and what the greater universe is like. Some may even seek out in-depth books like *Parallel Worlds* by Michio Kaku, or *The Elegant Universe* by Brian Greene. (That's the one that got me started on all this.) Still other people will devour videos, take classes, read this book and argue with everything I say here. Of the latter, I couldn't be happier, because it means they are engaged.

Finally, some—I hope many—will be drawn to the Bible to understand the parallels between the record of God's word and the universe as it unfolds before the greatest minds in history.

String physics' requirement of additional dimensions opens tremendous possibilities. Science is going in directions that have no barriers in conventional reality as we know it, and no allegiance to the established laws of physics. Each discovery spawns a dozen greater questions. How does gravity work in 11 dimensions? Does the same law of conservation of energy even exist in additional dimensions? How many of the infinitely possible frequencies to produce matter are occurring in additional dimensions? What exists in these extra dimensions? Where did I lose my car keys?

Brian Greene says that it is not beyond possibility that tiny civilizations exist in these tiny dimensions. Move over, Lilliputians. Science has arrived!

> *Our inability to probe distances smaller than a billionth of a billionth of a meter permits not only extra dimensions, but all manner of whimsical possibilities as well – even a microscopic civilization populated by even tinier people.*

> *The Elegant Universe*, Brian Greene, pg. 201

Tiny civilizations? Maybe Horton really did hear a Who. While tiny civilizations may sound absurd and Mr. Greene may have written his statement somewhat tongue in cheek, it is correct to think that something exists in these tiny curled-up dimensions. If the same vibrating strings that make up our three-dimensional universe exist in these tiny, undetectable dimensions, who are we to say that some type of life form does not exist there. The questions are endless; the possibilities are infinite. Anything goes. There is no scientific proof that rejects the possibility that life forms dwell in extra dimensions.

God

We started our quest seeking connections between science and the detailed historical records of the Bible, spanning thousands of years. The accounts in the Bible about a Creator, angels and a heavenly realm gain credibility when aligned with the phenomena of modern science.

The Bible testified of additional dimensions long before it became avant garde in the world of physics. For example, science now lends itself to answering an age-old question of theologians and philosophers: If God created the universe from nothing, then did God exist outside of nothing? If there was absolutely nothing before our universe was created, how could God be present in nothing? Understanding the possibility of extra dimensions, we now have a means to accept that God was able to create a three-dimensional universe while existing outside the universe he created. God can exist in any number of multiple dimensions.

In addition, the Bible says that God has the ability to observe people along with all his creation. With additional dimensions, is this ability any different from the example used in Flatville where people in three dimensions had the ability to see all of the two-dimensional Flatville? John and Suzy were limited to their two-dimensional universe. From their perspective, they knew all they could. By adding a third dimension, we had the advantage of observing their universe beyond their capability. Conceivably, God existing in 11 dimensions (or more) would have the capability of observing 100% of our three-dimensional world and still have perspectives beyond our wildest imaginations.

Here are a few scriptures referencing God creating the universe and observing His creation. I encourage you to read these and consider all we have discussed so far.

> *In the beginning, God created the heavens and the earth.*
>
> *Genesis 1:1*

> *In the beginning was the Word, and the Word was with God, and the Word was God. He [Jesus] was in the beginning with God. All things came into being through Him, and apart from Him nothing came into being that has come into being.*
>
> *John 1:1-3*

> *For by Him all things were created, both in the heavens and on earth, visible and invisible, whether thrones or dominions or rulers or authorities—all things have been created through Him and for Him.*
>
> *Colossians 1:16*

> By faith we understand that the worlds were prepared
> by the word of God, so that what is seen was not made out of
> things which are visible.
>
> *Hebrews 11:3*

> For He looks to the ends of the earth and sees everything
> under the heavens. When He imparted weight to the wind
> and meted out the waters by measure, When He set a limit for
> the rain and a course for the thunderbolt, Then He saw it and
> declared it; He established it and also searched it out.
>
> *Job 28:24-27*

> And there is no creature hidden from His sight, but all
> things are open and laid bare to the eyes of Him with whom
> we have to do.
>
> *Hebrews 4:13*

Heavenly Realms

The Bible does not stop at God. It also describes a heavenly realm where God dwells. There are over 600 accounts addressing a place called *Heaven*. Some verses are described from God's perspective, while others are from dreams, visions or the Holy Spirit. Heaven is a realm that we cannot see in everyday life. Yet it is not beyond the realm of possibilities of string physics that Heaven exists in extra dimensions.

> Micaiah said, "Therefore, hear the word of the LORD. I
> saw the LORD sitting on His throne, and all the host of heaven
> standing on His right and on His left."
>
> *2 Chronicles 18:18*

> The LORD is in His holy temple; the LORD'S throne is
> in heaven; His eyes behold, His eyelids test the sons of men.
>
> *Psalm 11:4*

> But being full of the Holy Spirit, he gazed intently into
> heaven and saw the glory of God, and Jesus standing at the
> right hand of God;
>
> *Acts 7:55*

For we know that if the earthly tent which is our house is torn down, we have a building from God, a house not made with hands, eternal in the heavens. For indeed in this house we groan, longing to be clothed with our dwelling from heaven,

2 Corinthians 5:1-2

After these things I looked, and behold, a door standing open in heaven, and the first voice which I had heard, like the sound of a trumpet speaking with me, said, "Come up here, and I will show you what must take place after these things." Immediately I was in the Spirit; and behold, a throne was standing in heaven, and One sitting on the throne.

Revelation 4:1-2

And every created thing which is in heaven and on the earth and under the earth and on the sea, and all things in them, I heard saying, "To Him who sits on the throne, and to the Lamb, be blessing and honor and glory and dominion forever and ever."

Revelation 5:13

Angels

There are nearly 300 passages addressing angels and other heavenly hosts. (I'm fairly certain there is at least one on the woman I married.) Interestingly, the Bible gives examples of angels existing in a heavenly realm as well as angels manifesting within our three-dimensional universe.

Here are a few scriptures on angels.

But the angel of the LORD called to him from heaven and said, Abraham, Abraham! And he said, "Here I am."

Genesis 22:11

He had a dream, and behold, a ladder was set on the earth with its top reaching to heaven; and behold, the angels of God were ascending and descending on it.

Genesis 28:12

> The angel answered and said to him, "I am Gabriel, who stands in the presence of God, and I have been sent to speak to you and to bring you this good news."
>
> *Luke 1:19*

> And an angel of the Lord suddenly stood before them, and the glory of the Lord shone around them; and they were terribly frightened. But the angel said to them, "Do not be afraid; for behold, I bring you good news of great joy which will be for all the people;"
>
> *Luke 2:9-10*

> And suddenly there appeared with the angel a multitude of the heavenly host praising God and saying, "Glory to God in the highest heaven, and on earth peace to those on whom his favor rests."
>
> *Luke 2:13-14*

> Do not neglect to show hospitality to strangers, for by this some have entertained angels without knowing it.
>
> *Hebrews 13:2*

> And I saw a strong angel proclaiming with a loud voice, "Who is worthy to open the book and to break its seals?"
>
> *Revelation 5:2*

God as Man

According to quantum and string physics, these advanced branches of physics scientifically open the door for the possibility of angels, heavenly hosts and the heavenly realm as described in the Bible. Let's revisit our two-dimensional homeland of Flatville as an example to see how this could be so. (See diagram 7.11)

If the heavenly realm and angels, as described in the Bible, exist in other dimensions, they could not appear to us completely in our three-dimensional universe. However, from time to time, it may be possible for beings from other dimensions (such as angels) to come into our three-dimensional brane, at which point, they could look a lot like people, just as the three-dimensional cube looked like the two-dimensional line people, when it entered Flatville. Science does not negate these possibilities.

Is it possible, then, for God to become like man? In John 10:30, Jesus declares that He is God, saying, "I and the Father are one." The Bible declares that Jesus came from Heaven and lived on the Earth as a man. Even so, many honest thinking people have a hard time understanding why God would come to earth in human form. If God is God, they say, why not just show up as God with all the Godly power? That sure would put to rest a lot of the issues Jesus faced. I'll admit, I used to wonder that myself.

Part of the answer lies in understanding that things from other dimensions that manifest in our three dimensions must abide by the laws of our three-dimensional world. This is precisely what Flatville demonstrates. Multi-dimensional beings exist as two-dimensional in Flatville. Taking this illustration further, particles from another dimension, revealed in our three-dimensional world, would have to fit within our 12 fundamental particles and/or our four force charges. In Chapter 3, we discussed how God manifests in our universe as light within the EMR spectrum. Since electromagnetism is one of the four forces, it makes theoretical sense that God could be established in our universe as light particles.

Theoretically, frequencies producing particles in, say, the sixth dimension, could not appear in our dimensions as the same six-dimensional things. Anything that is expressed in our three dimensions must be formed from a combination of the 12 fundamental particles of matter and/or four force charges. This is borne of science and points to an answer for why and how Christ manifested on earth as a man; showing up fully manifest as God just wouldn't fit, nor could we have seen him as such. Perhaps that is why John 1:10 says, *He was in the world, and though the world was made through him, the world did not recognize him.*

To address this, let's go back to Flatville and diagram 7.13. If Jesus, existing in all theoretically predicted 11 dimensions, came to Earth, it is probable he would only manifest in the three dimensions of this universe. Similar to the cubes breaking the two-dimensional plane (diagram 7.12), where only two of the three dimensions could be observed by the people of Flatville; only three dimensions of Jesus' total dimensions would be manifested in our three-dimensional universe. Jesus (as God) would still exist above and/or below the three-dimensional plane in fullness. However, the people on Earth would only perceive him within the limitations of the three-dimensional universe. Just as they could not picture a tesseract, neither could they picture a multi-dimensional God.

To stay in line with the requirements of the three-dimensional manifestation, Jesus would have to be revealed on Earth within the limitations of the 12 particles of matter and/or four force charges. Obviously, people meet these same requirements. We are comprised of the fundamental particles that make atoms. I suppose Jesus could have come to Earth as a horse, or a dog or a centaur for that matter. However, if Jesus came to Earth within the limitations of three dimensions to communicate with humans, doesn't it just make sense he would be expressed as a person? (People buy from people. Talking dogs... not so much.)

If you read the teachings of Jesus, he taught more than salvation. Although salvation is arguably the most important message, Jesus tried to communicate that we are more—much more—than we can see, hear, touch and taste. Like the characters in the movie *The Matrix*, Jesus came to liberate the world from vast deception over our identity. He taught us that we are more than three-dimensional creatures bound to this universe. In truth, he seemed to be saying that we could be like him.

Jesus not only performed miracles, he told us that we have the authority to heal people as well. I have been in awe on many occasions witnessing supernatural healings taking effect before my eyes. Yep, I've seen it, and I'm a skeptical guy. It takes a lot to convince me. I remember being prayed for, and my broken rib from a hockey incident instantly healed—healed to the point where it went from incredible pain to no pain at all, from not being able to move my arms to swinging my arms around in large violent circles. Yeah, it gets real, really fast when it happens to you. Jesus taught us that we have a spiritual aspect to our beings, and there is much more to this universe than three dimensions. What if one or more of the dimensions is called *spiritual*?

*And as you go, preach, saying, "The kingdom of heaven
is at hand." Heal the sick, raise the dead, cleanse the lepers,
cast out demons. Freely you received, freely give.*

Matthew 10:7-8

*Truly I say to you, whoever says to this mountain, "Be
taken up and cast into the sea," and does not doubt in his
heart, but believes that what he says is going to happen, it
will be granted him.*

Mark 11:23

*Whatever city you enter and they receive you, eat what
is set before you; and heal those in it who are sick, and say to
them, "The kingdom of God has come near to you."*

Luke 10:9-10

*But the Helper, the Holy Spirit, whom the Father will
send in My name, He will teach you all things, and bring to
your remembrance all that I said to you.*

John 14:26

Death and Resurrection

The concept of extra dimensions of string theory makes the
extraordinary idea of rising from the dead possible, because theoretically,
it is possible to move in and out of extra dimensions. Like the cubes in
diagram 7.12, if Jesus (as God) exists in 11 dimensions, he could have
come to Earth manifest in three dimensions while still existing in all 11
dimensions. If the cube went completely through Flatville, then the cube
would disappear. If then the cube came back up through Flatville, it would
once again manifest itself in Flatville as a two-dimensional object. Likewise,
it is possible that Jesus passed through our three-dimensional brane and
then re-entered our brane. This is one possible scientific explanation of
death and resurrection—not just for Jesus, but for all of us.

Jesus foretold the process of His upcoming death and resurrection to
His disciples.

> *For He [Jesus] was teaching His disciples and telling*
> *them, 'The Son of Man is to be betrayed into the hands of*
> *men, and they will kill Him; and when He has been killed,*
> *He will rise three days later.' But they [disciples] did not*
> *understand this statement, and they were afraid to ask Him.*
>
> *Mark 9:31-32*

Another possible explanation of resurrection harkens back to how atoms go in and out of wave probabilities and particles. Recall that part of you could be on the moon right now, because your particles were transitioning in and out of the localized, particle realm? There are portions of your atoms in the wave state spread throughout the universe, with a remote chance of you dematerializing here on Earth and re-materializing on the moon. As crazy as it sounds, according to quantum physics, it is possible Jesus could die and then come back to life in this manner. Now, if you happen to be God and have the ability to control wave collapse, this process of going in and out of our realm would be relatively easy.

The idea of dying and coming back from the dead is too difficult a possibility for some skeptics. Even in today's world, with all our knowledge of quantum and string physics, some people will decide it isn't possible. Many people in Jesus' day did not believe him, and many followers fell away from his teaching. Some people would rather believe in aliens than believe that God came to our three-dimensional universe as a man.

Sometimes We Just Don't Get It

Reflecting on Jesus coming to Earth, it's as if he went to Flatville and told them they wore a polka dot dress and Suzy believed him but John didn't. She believed there was more to her world, even though she did not fully understand how. In theology, we would say that Suzy had faith. John on the other hand, did not understand the concept of polka dot dresses and therefore thought the messenger was wrong. Similarly, some people believe Jesus was God who came to our three dimensions, and part of that journey included bringing information about other realms. Over the centuries, some people believed by faith in the message from Jesus, and some people did not. Fair enough.

Not everyone who heard Jesus' message believed in what he tried to communicate. And like the trouble we had with the earlier example of trying to explain to Suzy and John what a polka dot dress is, Jesus had problems expounding on the concepts of things such as the heavenly realm, authority over disease, and mankind's relationship with God. He spent a lot of his time communicating through analogies, parables and metaphors. Scriptures reveal there were occasions when Jesus was frustrated at humanity's inability to capture the truth about the "great beyond."

> *Therefore, I speak to them in parables; because while seeing they do not see, and while hearing they do not hear, nor do they understand.*
>
> *Matthew 13:13*

> *And He answered them and said, 'O unbelieving generation, how long shall I be with you? How long shall I put up with you? Bring him to Me!'*
>
> *Mark 9:19*

> *And He was saying, He who has ears to hear, let him hear.*
>
> *Mark 4:9*

> *And when you see a south wind blowing, you say, 'It will be a hot day,' and it turns out that way. You hypocrites! You know how to analyze the appearance of the earth and the sky, but why do you not analyze this present time?*
>
> *Luke 12:55-56*

> *If I told you earthly things and you do not believe, how shall you believe if I tell you heavenly things?*
>
> *John 3:12*

> *Why do you not understand what I am saying? It is because you cannot hear My word.*
>
> *John 8:43*

Sometimes We Believe by Faith

Jesus told his followers there is a heavenly realm which humans inhabit when they die. This begs the question: do we go to Heaven, or is part of us already in Heaven? There are scriptures that inform us that we live in both the body and the spirit. The Bible also informs us that God, Jesus and the Holy Spirit dwell in us in a spiritual sense. So, does co-living in a spiritual sense mean we also exist within extra dimensions? It is scientifically possible that while alive, we exist in more than three dimensions?

If we exist in more than three dimensions, then what happens when we die? As crazy as it sounds, it is possible that when we die, we continue to exist in the other dimensions. A portion of us may cease to be perceived in these three dimensions. However, we could be perceived in completely different ways in these other dimensions. And these additional dimensions could very well be what is described in the Bible as Heaven.

Just as quantum and string physics are forcing us to rethink the laws of physics and the writings of the Bible, so also, we need to reconsider what we think of as death. Are we ceasing to exist in every sense of the word, or are we merely—perhaps gloriously—transitioning to other dimensions, other forms of existence?

We have quantum and string physics educating the world about collapsing waves, invisible realms, parallel universes, vibrating strands of energy and additional dimensions. Science has a glimpse of what is happening outside the three spatial dimensions, and is finding that we are the people of Flatville.

Believing in God is not the only thing that takes faith. Science has acquired the same problem Jesus had—teaching humanity they exist in ways beyond what they can comprehend. Some people have faith that science is correct, or at least going in the right direction. Others are not so quick to get on board. They are taking a "wait and see" attitude. Which one are you? Although someone can choose not to believe in quantum or string physics, the amount of supporting evidence prevents anyone from taking a position that the concepts of quantum and string physics cannot be *possible*.

Let me stress that none of this *proves* that God and angels and Heaven exist. Instead, I am making the case that quantum and string physics support the *possibility* that God, angels and Heaven can exist. If they can exist, then atheism is dead, because atheism rests on the impossibility of these things existing. Recall that unlike agnosticism, atheism says absolutely there is no God. Agnosticism says we aren't sure. In order for atheism to reign supreme, it has to prove there is no God.

When it comes to quantum and string physics, there is rapidly accumulating evidence of God's presence as described in the Bible.

Chapter 8

~~~~~~~~~~~~~~~~~~~~~~~~~~~~~~

Time

Synchronized Repetition

Our lives revolve around time. We wish we had more time; we are rushed for time; we are ahead of the times, behind the times, in a race for time, or having the time of our life. But what exactly is time? That is a good question—one that science has a hard time answering consistently. Everyone seems to know what time is until asked to explain it.

First off, when we think of time, we usually consider different measurements of time: days, hours, minutes, seconds, etc. These are really measures of *synchronized repetition*. The most common way to accurately measure synchronized repetition is with some form of clock. Clocks allow us to break time into increments and gather data so we can use it for our convenience. They come in all types: sundial, quartz watch, atomic clock and light clock. Some ancient cultures even kept time by burning a vertical rope, marking increments with evenly spaced knots.

In the pursuit of perfect synchronized repetition, humans excel at keeping time of things. Sporting events track runners to a thousandth of a second. The current 100-yard dash world record holder, Usain Bolt of Jamaica, has a record time of 9.572 seconds. But that kind of accuracy pales in comparison to what the U.S. Government does with time. The U.S. Time Service Department (yes, they actually pay people to keep track of time) has 20 cesium clocks, 18 hydrogen maser clocks and 4 rubidium fountain clocks for the purpose of accuracy. In fact, many countries spend taxpayers' money on keeping time. There are even international conferences so everyone can agree on time.

Cesium clocks used to be the top of the market for clocks, being accurate to within 1 billionth of a second, but they have since been outdone by hydrogen masers and rubidium fountains. A rubidium fountain clock is accurate to within 300 trillionths of a second, meaning it would only be off by 1 second every 100 million years. So why all the fuss over trillionths of a second? As it turns out, accuracy is very important for things like Global Positioning Satellite (GPS) capability. The technology is extremely complicated and time accuracy is vital; every billionth of a second discrepancy equates to a 1-foot error. This might not seem much of a problem for driving around in the city, but being off by even 10 nanoseconds (10^{-8} seconds) could cause the military to miss its target and kill innocent civilians.

You would think time increments couldn't get any shorter than 300 trillionths of a second, but you would be wrong. The shortest span of time is believed to be a Planck second, or 10^{-43} seconds. It is the time it takes for light to travel a Planck length. This simply means there are 10,000,000,000,000,000,000,000,000,000,000,000,000,000,000 Planck seconds, or synchronized repetitions, in 1 second. Recall that, in Chapter 2, we discussed how physics describes the first developments of the big bang in Planck seconds. (Note: the only span possibly shorter than a Planck second is a New York minute, but science is divided on its exact value.)

The human race as we know it would be lost without time as a guide. We rely on time to help us meet friends for coffee or get to that important job interview. Time can be as important as location. After all, what good is it knowing *where* to meet if you have no idea *when* the other party will be there.

Times Flows from Past to Future

The concept of time goes further than what a clock communicates. Time can be segmented into three categories: past, present and future. Humans have an innate sense that time moves from the past to the future, this has been coined the *flow of time* or *arrow of time*. People are born, they become toddlers, teenagers, adults and finally seniors. We move along on a prescribed timeline from one stage to the next. It would be strange if people started out as adults, then became infants, then seniors and eventually teenagers. Our perception of time flow revolves around almost everything we engage in. A baseball game starts with inning 1 and moves along to the 9th inning. Our workday starts at 9:00am and ends at 5:00pm. The sun rises in the morning and sets in the evening.

In order to distinguish the past from the future, we use the present. Undoubtedly, whatever age you are now, you knew that a moment ago you were younger and in another moment you will be older. We always seem to exist in the present. If you think about your birthday party of last year, the memory of the past is relived at the present moment. You don't physically leave *now* and go back in time to revisit the event. Similarly, if you visualize what you are going to talk about during an upcoming date with the person of your dreams, it doesn't materially happen at that moment of imagining because the future event hasn't occurred yet. Every thought and action revolves around the now.

Whether we are engaged in science, sports, economy, health or book writing, humans base their activities on the concept of past, present and future. Science describes the universe starting with the big bang, leading to the present universe and projecting into the future. Sporting events have a starting gun, a whistle or a first pitch. They end with a checkered flag, a buzzer or finish line. Economists track and predict stock prices, being sure to warn us that past performance does not guarantee future results. And your doctor assesses symptoms and treats your illness based on how you were, how you are, and how you want to be. Time is how we make sense of the world around us. As such, we are wholly dependent on it.

God Relevance

Okay, so we have clocks to measure synchronous repetition, and we understand there is a past, present and future, but what does time have to do with supporting the existence of God? Everything. As it turns out, the Bible makes some interesting claims about God which have direct relevance to the concept of time. For example, the Bible says that God knows a person's every thought, yet it also indicates that God is surprised at peoples' actions. So how can God both know and be surprised?

To further complicate things, the Bible has accounts of God knowing future events, saying that God governs time. There are also theologians who interpret the Bible as saying God is timeless—outside of time—and that God is eternal. Still others claim God must be actively involved within time, experiencing it with us.

As we will see, the subject of time has a lot to do with the existence of God.

Let's start with some Bible passages directed towards God/Christ being all knowing, knowing future events and also being surprised. These accounts support that God, at the very least, actively communicates with creation.

...God is greater than our heart and knows all things.

1 John 3:20b

Now I [Christ] have told you before it happens, so that when it happens, you may believe.

John 14:29

When you hear of wars and disturbances, do not be terrified; for these things must take place first, but the end does not follow immediately." Then He continued by saying to them, "Nation will rise against nation and kingdom against kingdom, and there will be great earthquakes, and in various places plagues and famines; and there will be terrors and great attesting miracles from heaven."

Luke 21:9-11

And He wondered at their unbelief. And He was going around the villages teaching.

Mark 6:6

Now when Jesus heard this, He marveled and said to those who were following, "Truly I say to you, I have not found such great faith with anyone in Israel."

Matthew 8:10

In addition, the Bible acknowledges that God perceives time differently than people, that he has the ability to govern time and to cause things to happen at specific times. There are also many passages that speak to the idea of eternity and that God and Christ are eternal.

> *But do not let this one fact escape your notice, beloved, that with the Lord one day is like a thousand years, and a thousand years like one day.*
>
> *2Peter 3:8*

> *But of that day and hour no one knows, not even the angels of heaven, nor the Son, but the Father alone.*
>
> *Matthew 24:26*

> *Then the LORD answered Job out of the whirlwind and said, "Who is this that darkens counsel by words without knowledge? Now gird up your loins like a man, And I will ask you, and you instruct Me! Where were you when I laid the foundation of the earth? Tell Me, if you have understanding, Who set its measurements? Since you know. Or who stretched the line on it? On what were its bases sunk? Or who laid its cornerstone,"*
>
> *Job 38:1-6*

> *Is anything too difficult for the LORD? At the appointed time I will return to you, at this time next year, and Sarah will have a son.*
>
> *Genesis 18:14*

> *Jesus Christ is the same yesterday and today and forever.*
>
> *Hebrews 13:8*

> *"I am the Alpha and the Omega," says the Lord God, "who is and who was and who is to come, the Almighty."*
>
> *Revelation 1:8*

> *Then Moses said to God, "Behold, I am going to the sons of Israel, and I will say to them, 'The God of your fathers has sent me to you.' Now they may say to me, 'What is His*

> *name?' What shall I say to them?" God said to Moses, "I AM*
> *WHO I AM"; and He said, "Thus you shall say to the sons of*
> *Israel, 'I AM has sent me to you.'"*
>
> *Exodus 3:13-14*

> *Now to the King eternal, immortal, invisible, the only*
> *God, be honor and glory forever and ever. Amen.*
>
> *1 Timothy 1:17*

In order for this study to be comprehensive, we must deal with time and see if science agrees with what the Bible has to say about time and the possibility of God.

Curveball

Time has been one of the most contested issues throughout history between theologians, philosophers and physicists. As we said earlier, theologians debate whether God is timeless, or within time but already knows all future events, or is actively involved with creation on a moment-by-moment basis. However, we can't address these theological positions until we understand the debates going on in physics and philosophy.

Time has been debated by philosophers and physicists since the beginning of…well, of time itself. All of the great (and a few not-so-great) minds have weighed in on what time *is* and how it works. The Greek philosopher Heraclitus saw the universe as dynamic, full of change. To him, time was secondary to change and motion. Another Greek, Parmenides, didn't think time existed at all, so he ruled out change. Plato addressed time by creating two worlds. He separated an eternal perfect world of the stars and planets—a world with no beginning—from a temporal, ever-changing and imperfect Earth where time emerges from eternity. Aristotle believed that everything in the natural world—to him, this was Earth—is within a past and present of time, and is subject to change. He thought of the heavens (stars, planets) differently than Earth, as something outside of time, and therefore not experiencing time or change.

Arising from these roots of ancient philosophy, modern philosophers have narrowed the debate into two primary distinctions: *presentism* and *eternalism*. Certainly, reams of documents exist, taking the discussion into far greater detail, however, to keep the subject matter simple, we'll concentrate on these two predominant divisions of thought.

Presentism is the belief that neither past nor future exist. Instead, there is only the present. One of the most famous theologians to hold this position is Augustine, who writes in Book XI of his *Confessions*:

> What is by now evident and clear is that neither future nor past exists, and it is inexact language three times, a present of things past, a present of things present, a present of things to come. In the soul there are these three aspects of time, and I do not see them anywhere else. The present considering the past is memory, the present considering the present is immediate awareness, the present considering the future is expectation.
>
> *Confessions,* St. Augustine 11:38

(One notation to make of Augustine: his dualistic beliefs on presentism revolve around our physical world, he believed that God is atemporal, outside of time, perfect and unchanging.)

According to presentism, the past and future are not real; only the present is real. People experience reality as a continuum of *now*-moments. It is not that the past did not exist, because at one point it existed as a specific now-moment. However, once a now-moment passes, it becomes the past and is no longer considered reality. Therefore, the universe consists of only *nows*. Take a moment and consider an event in your past. It can only occur while you exist in a present physical state. Only in the *now* are you able to be influenced by the past, such as laughing or crying over a memory. The presentism view says memories are experienced as a present-past. Any recollections always occur during a person's *now*. There is no way to go back into the past, so it cannot exist.

The future doesn't exist either, according to presentism, because you can only think of the future from your state of *now*—the present-future. There is no way to physically go into the future, because that would mean that you would have to leave your physical *now*. And there is no way to be in two *nows* at the same time. When imagining a future event, you remain in the physical *now*, imagining the possibilities of what may be forthcoming.

Consider a baseball player in the dugout, visualizing his upcoming at-bat. He pictures himself in the batter's box, the approaching ball as it whirls through the air. He imagines eyeing the flight, swinging the bat and making contact. Home run! But in his mental imaging, does he leave his present location and place in time, and go into the future at-bat? Presentism says *no*; he went through the visualization in his *now* even though he imagined what a future scene might be like.

To most people, presentism makes sense.

Eternalism, the second philosophy, is sometimes referred to as *block time* or *block universe*. It believes that the past, present and future are all equally real, and that all spacetime exists as a single block of spacetime. Time is incorporated with the three dimensions of space: length, width and depth. Imagine a big cube, and inside is the universe, including every moment of time from the big bang to the end of the world.

With no distinction to separate past, present and future, eternalism concludes that the universe has already been determined from the inception of the big bang to the end of the universe billions of years from now—however one defines "the end." That block of spacetime includes you, your life, your past, present and future; it has already been played out in this all-inclusive block time.

At first glance, eternalism is difficult to grasp. It's perplexing that anyone would think this way. Who in their right mind would say there is no distinction between the past, present and future? Well, Einstein did. Einstein threw the ultimate curveball when his theories of special relativity and general relativity rocked the world in the early 1900's, proving that there is no arrow of time, no past, present or future.

Time-reversal Symmetry vs Entropy

Being notoriously indifferent to man's efforts to understand it, physics offers a casual, "So what?" to our attempts to define time, choosing instead to do what it wants to do. In the world of physics, time goes equally in either direction: past to future, or future to past. Whether it be

Newton's equations of gravity, Maxwell's equations of electromagnetism, or Einstein's calculations for special relativity and general relativity, all are treated equally whether they are going backward or forward in time. Physics has put its foot down—the "flow of time" is a human construct and doesn't exist in reality.

> *There is nothing that corresponds to a flow of time,*
> *a movement of time, a past, present, and future, or now...*
> *None of that is there in physics.*
>
> *In Search of Time*, Dan Falk, St. Martin's
> Press, New York 2008, pg. 274

One particular area where the realm of physics doesn't favor the flow of time is with the concept of *time-reversal symmetry*, where there is no distinction between going forward or backward in time. Time-reversal symmetry says that if you were to reverse the value of all velocities of a system by their negative values, then the system will reverse exactly on the same trajectory it had originally taken. For example, take a system... say, an egg. Now imagine it accidentally bumped and rolls off the counter, splattering all over the floor. Most people would expect the egg mess to sit there until someone cleaned it up. According to time-reversal symmetry, if you were able to reverse all velocities of that system, then the egg whites, yoke and fractured shell would all travel to a common spot on the floor where they assemble back into a perfectly formed egg that pops back up to the counter and gently rolls to a safe spot.

(Note, the egg didn't reform on its own. There had to be an energy catalyst, i.e. a breeze or floor vibrations, that invested in the process, for the egg to reform exactly as it was before it splattered. However, there also had to be an original energy catalyst for the egg sitting on the counter to roll off in the first place.)

Of course, splattered eggs reversing into a perfectly formed egg sounds impossible. While physicists would agree it is extremely unlikely, mathematics says that it is possible. And because egg-reversal is conceivable, physics can claim there is scientific proof to dispel the idea of a flow of time. But not all is lost for those who prescribe to the notion of time moving from past to future, because physicists are divided on this issue. There is something called *entropy* that gives time-reversal symmetry some problems and supports a notion of arrow of time.

Entropy, also known as the *second law of thermodynamics*, says that systems move from an orderly state to a disorderly state. We digest food, converting molecularly orderly substances to less orderly forms of energy and waste; an ice cube melts into a liquid; an egg falls off the counter and splatters into a mess. These are all examples of entropy in action.

For clarification, entropy and order are polar opposites. Saying *high entropy* means a low degree of order. Conversely, a low degree of entropy means a high degree of order. So when the egg on the counter with its shell intact moved to the floor and became messy, it moved from a high order state (low entropy) to a low order state (high entropy). Essentially, if you are high on order, you are low on entropy, and vise-versa.

A simplified way to think of entropy is to use numbers. Let's say you spend hours writing a romantic 14-page letter to your loved one but before you can share it, an argument flares as they often do in the throes of love. In frustration, you toss the pages into the air, watching them chaotically flutter to the floor. But things calm quickly. It turns out the argument was a miscommunication—she really *is* a Seahawks fan—so you reconcile in a sweet embrace. Suddenly remembering your testament of eternal affection, you run to gather the pages littering the floor. To your horror, the pieces are not in order. In fact, for a 14 page letter, there is only 1 correct order compared with 87,178,291,199 possibilities for being out of order (assuming they all landed right side up). The subject of entropy naturally arises as you and your sweetie spend the rest of the afternoon putting the pieces back together.

In our story of star-crossed lovers and the tossed 14-page letter, they had a 1-in-87 billion chance of low entropy and high order (finding the pages in correct sequence) and an 87 billion-to-1 chance of high entropy and low order (a chaotic mess leading to couple's therapy). Now, to put things into perspective, consider how many subatomic particles are in an egg—a lot more than 14. If an egg falls on the floor, it will certainly splatter into a big mess of high disorder and low entropy.

Of course, there are limits to disorder—physics calls this *equilibrium*. This is when entropy has reached its maximum value. At this point, you don't notice any further changes between order and disorder. Pour a cup of hot water into a cup of cold water, and entropy will have the cold water warming and the hot water cooling until they both reach a common temperature where there is no more thermal change. Even though the water molecules continue to move about the cup, these changes in location have little effect on the entropy of the temperature.

Entropy is said to have reached *maximum value* when things stop displaying noticeable change. If you picked up the 14-page love letter already in random order and threw it back into the air, you wouldn't obtain any more entropy—they are already in maximum disorder. What is the difference if the first toss landed as order possibility #3,734,566 out of 87 billion, and the second toss landed as possibility #22,777,981 out of the same 87 billion? None. Messed up is messed up!

Hopefully you see the conundrum. On the one hand, we have physics telling us that a disorderly splattered egg can miraculously reform into a highly ordered egg. Using the love letter example, it would be as though you picked up the jumbled pages, threw them in the air, and in a 1-in-87 billion chance, you had all pages land in the exact order needed. On the other hand, physics says this occurrence would go against the second law of thermodynamics, and that once the pages are muddled, they remain in disarray. On this contested issue it seems that both sides are theoretically correct.

For our purposes, we must note that the principle of entropy ends up supporting the notion of an arrow of time. Physicists have traced the origin of entropy back to the big bang when the universe started with the highest order (lowest entropy). In fact, some physicists have gone as far as to say that the moment the universe began as a singularity (Chapter 2), the universe was in a perfect orderly state—a condition physicists call *perfect symmetry*. The universe was so perfect that it had to become imperfect for the universe to develop.

The universe was beautiful, symmetrical, but rather useless. Life as we know it could not exist in this perfect state.

*In order for the possibility of life to exist, the symmetry of the
universe had to break as it cooled.*

Parallel Worlds, Michio Kaku, pg.98

At the exact moment of the big bang, the universe had the highest
order it will ever have. Since that moment, the universe as a whole
continues to become increasingly disorganized, just as the law of entropy
tells us it should. Entropy gives us a reference for the disorder as we move
through time. In simple terms, think of the universe as going in a direction
of 1, 2, 3, 4, 5, 6…, with increasing numbers signifying increasing entropy
(decreasing order). This process of consistent change allows us to gauge
what occurred in the past and what may occur in the future. Understanding
entropy, we have a good idea that 7 and 8 will be coming, and that it will
be more disorderly than 1 and 2, but not as bad as 16.

Because entropy naturally progresses from order (low entropy) to
disorder (high entropy), it provides a basis for understanding the constant
movement of change. Hence, we are able to comprehend what physics
calls *arrow of time.* Without the law of entropy, everything (not just the
egg) would go in and out of disorder with no rhyme or reason. Instead
of 1, 2, 3, 4, 5, 6…, the universe's order would go 4, 1, 6, 2, 5, 3….,
making it impossible to make reliable predictions about the past or future.
Fortunately, the universe doesn't do that. Its entropy flows in an orderly
fashion.

Hopefully, the importance of entropy is making sense, but let me toss
in a small monkey wrench. For astute readers, we must acknowledge that
not everything is moving from a highly ordered condition to a chaotic state.
A good example of this is life on Earth, where orderly life forms such as
humans appeared after a less orderly planet existed. This is in contrast to
the easy-to-comprehend 1, 2, 3… progression.

This illustrates that entropy is not an absolute. The law of entropy
says that systems tend to go from order to disorder. It does not claim that
every system must or will do so in a straightforward manner. Rather, the
universe as a whole moves toward disorder. As a collective whole, the
universe abides by the 1, 2, 3, 4, 5, 6… progression of entropy. But the
universe is a big place. Where it experiences increasing entropy in most

areas, it allows flexibility for order to come out of disorder in other areas. It permits pockets like our little corner of the universe for highly ordered systems of plants, animals and humans to exist—subsystems within the whole that move from disorder to order.

The essential ingredient to moving from disorder to order in violation of the law of entropy is the investment of energy. If you tell a teenager to clean his room, unless he invests energy into the process, the room will continue to progress from order to disorder and eventually be condemned by the Board of Health.

Consider the fate of our resurrected egg. It went from high disorder (a splattered mess), to order (miraculously reforming as a whole egg), to disorder when someone cooked scrambled eggs for breakfast.

Going from naturally occurring entropy to reverse entropy happens all the time. Humans have an insatiable appetite to induce manmade reverse-entropy systems for our conveniences. Houses don't build themselves. Cars are the result of massive infusions of energy, from refining the raw ore for steel to weaving cotton for the fuzzy dice. And while apples grow on trees, it takes water, soil and sunshine to produce the final result.

Now, while the example of the egg retracing its exact trajectories is remote, you might be surprised at how often cases of time-reversal symmetry actually occur. The other day I was talking about it with a friend of mine—a physics professor who happens to be agnostic. I shared how I had cracked a rib playing hockey on a Thursday evening. The pain shot through my body like bolts of lightning. It lasted a moment and then subsided, but it left me wondering what would set off the next flash of agony. Of course, my friend only wanted to know if I'd made the shot, which I did, of course. Unfortunately, the medical field has no procedure (like a cast) for broken ribs. You just wait out the natural healing process of 6-8 weeks and stay off the ice in the meantime.

I continued sharing how I took the next day (Friday) off work, but had a very important meeting on Saturday morning, so I endured the pain as my wife drove us there. (After all, I am a hockey player.) After close to 2 hours of witnessing me wince in pain with the slightest movement my friends insisted on praying for my broken rib to be healed before leaving the meeting. Lo and behold, it was healed right then and there! I don't mean a gradual healing. I mean I stood up and started waving my arms in huge circles to prove the pain was gone. On our way home that day, my wife and I went to Costco for supplies, she wanted me to stay in the car and take it easy but I insisted I was good to go and found myself lifting heavy cases of water, and using the shopping cart like an oversized scooter proving my ribs were still okay.

My professor friend looked at me and said that he didn't have a problem with the ribs reforming back to a normal, healed condition, because he understood entropy and time-reversal symmetry. However, he did have a problem figuring out how prayer might have helped the cause. Needless to say, he can't wait to read this book.

Einstein's Spacetime

Entropy has given science a basis for supporting this inherent sense people have of time moving from past to future. Now it's time to look at time from Einstein's perspective. To understand the position of physics, we need to understand two perspectives of time. First, is time itself when it is not associated with the three spatial dimensions of length, width and depth. The second perspective is when time *is* associated with length, width and depth. The latter is what Einstein declared as *spacetime.*

When physics studies time in the first perspective—not associated with spatial dimensions—it runs smack into a huge problem: it doesn't actually describe anything. Think about it. What does it mean when we say one hour is one hour? It's like printing money with no other basis than everybody accepts it. The weird thing with time is it becomes a circular reference; i.e., it defines itself. Time does not have the same tangible qualities that, say, length or width have. Although measurements of length are given arbitrary names like inch, meter or mile, when you measure 100 yards in length you can actually see what 100 yards represents. (The distance the Cleveland Browns can't seem to travel on any given Sunday) In contrast to time's circular references, spatial dimensions leave us with something more meaningful than, "100 yards means 100 yards."

So if time does have a tangible quality, what or where is it? Let's use the analogy of a river. A river flows downstream and we can measure its flow rate: perhaps 1,000 gallons per minute (GPM). Another way is to measure distance by watching a stick float from upstream point A to downstream point B. By measuring the distance from points A to B, we actually measured the river by spatial factors. Now try to imagine time without spatial dimensions. What does 1 hour act like? It would act no different than 1 Planck second or 1 day or 1 millennium because without space there is nothing to act upon. The same thing goes for past, present and future. Without spatial dimensions, they are all the same.

In everyday life, no one cares that time is circular or that we can't find it; we just want to know that the game is at 7:00pm, bedtime is at 11pm and the alarm clock will start screaming at 5:30 am.

People usually make use of time from the second perspective by adding it to spatial dimensions. If you have an upcoming business meeting, you get the spatial and time coordinates, such as: 123 Main Street (longitude and latitude), suite 301 (altitude), on Monday, January 11th at 2:00pm (time). It wouldn't make sense to have a meeting on Monday, January 11th at 2:00pm with no location - you wouldn't know where to meet.

Einstein established that time is dependent upon reference frames and spatial position. To Einstein, in order to make sense of time, we need to look at it from the second perspective—time along with length, height and depth. He called it spacetime because time is not separate from the three spatial dimensions. Once unified with length, height and depth, spacetime became what we now know as the fourth dimension.

A very interesting thing happened when Einstein merged time with the spatial dimensions. He discovered that things witness a different passage of time depending on how fast something is moving. The faster something is moving, the slower it experiences the passage of time. Conversely, the slower something is moving, the faster it experiences the passage of time. This is where the term relativity comes in. The passage of time is relative to an individual object dependent upon its speed. This means that if I walk along a path at 3 miles per hour, time would actually pass more quickly for me than for John zooming along in a rocket at 50,000 miles per hour. (Time flies when you're having fun!)

Light has One More Trick up its Sleeve

When it comes to understanding time and its relevance to God, we find that light has one more trick up its sleeve. Back in Einstein's day, physicists were trying to figure out whether light was waves or particles. They finally concluded that light acted in both capacities. As Einstein studied light, he focused on one of its unusual traits—light travels at a constant speed of 186,281 miles per second and nothing in the universe can go faster. (Technically, light travels at this speed in a vacuum. However, for simplicity, I'll refer to this speed also occurring within space, as do most physicists when discussing light.)

Scientists also know what the slowest thing in the universe is. It is us. Well, anything that has mass, which includes up quarks, down quarks and electrons. To reach the ultimate speed of sloth, an object has to be what physicists call *at rest*. It's easy to be *at rest*. Yes, lounging on your couch on Sunday afternoon qualifies as being *at rest*, but so does driving along at 60 miles per hour.

The important thing for an *at rest* condition is maintaining a constant speed with the things around you. What would happen if while driving at a constant speed of 60 mph, you accidentally dropped the donut you were about to stuff in your mouth? It would fall directly into your lap, no different than if you were sitting on your sofa. In contrast, if you stuck your hand out the window and dropped it, you and that glazed ring would rapidly part company.

This is because inside the car, you and everything around you is moving at a constant speed, so you don't notice any difference between being in the car or on the sofa. Meanwhile, a policeman sees you speeding along in a 40-mph zone as you clean up the donut mess. From the policeman's relative position, you are not in the same motion perspective as he is, and therefore you are not at rest. At least, not until he pulls you over to ask if you have an extra doughnut.

This is why you don't feel dizzy even though Earth is spinning at 1,000 mph at the equator. Have you noticed the lack of a constant stiff breeze blowing through your hair as Earth is traveling around the sun at some 67,000 mph? Of course not. Yet, these non-existent effects are nothing compared to the solar system flying through the galaxy at over 450,000 mph. We don't feel anything of this. Why? Because motion is relative.

Being *at rest* is when objects are in a state of constant motion— neither accelerating nor decelerating. This is why we don't feel the spin of Earth, its orbit around the sun or your motion relative to your speeding Porsche. Now if you were to hit the brakes at a red-light or if the Earth would suddenly decrease its spin, the change in relative speeds would significantly disrupt your *at rest* state. Donuts would hit dashboards and people would topple to the ground all over the world.

Anything with mass can be at rest, but light, having zero mass, technically is never at rest. It always moves at the constant speed of 671 million miles per hour (mph). This is the kind of stuff that made Einstein a celebrity. Again, light always goes the same speed.

This fact presents some interesting scenarios. Let's say your car has the awesome ability to go 100 million mph. If you turn on the headlights, the light still shoots forth at a rate of 671 million mph, not 571 million mph, as most people would think. Light stays constant. Even if we drove wildly in reverse at 100 million mph, the headlights would cut through the night at the same speed of 671 million mph. Light is not relative to anything. It is the universal independent agent.

Physics doesn't work like that for the rest of us. We are always moving relative to other things. If you were chasing me at 60 mph and I was fleeing at 20 mph, you would be gaining on me at a rate of 40 mph (60-20 = 40), and it wouldn't be long until I was road kill. My speed of 20 mph is relative to your speed of 60 mph. If you put your car in reverse at 60 mph and I continued to run in the opposite direction at 20 mph, we would distance ourselves at 80 mph (60 + 20 = 80) and I would get away, relatively speaking.

Time Dilation

Let's summarize. So far, science says:

1. Nothing moves faster than light and nothing moves
   slower than objects (us) while at rest

2. Light always travels at a constant speed while
objects (like us) always travel a speed relative
to the speed of other objects around us

3. The faster something travels the slower it
experiences the passage of time

This third point needs further explanation, to do so we need to discuss Einstein's theory of special relativity regarding time dilation. The heart of the theory is that the faster something approaches the speed the light, the more space contracts and time slows down. In diagram 8.1a, if we look into space, planet A and planet B are 100 thousand light years apart. It would take 8 billion years for a rocket traveling at 7 million mph (1% the speed of light) to get from one planet to the other.

As the rocket takes billions of years to go from planet A to planet B, watching from Earth we perceive time going by at 1 hour per 1 hour. However, if we leave Earth and get into the rocket ship, press the pedal to the metal and whizz along at 99.99999% the speed of light, something weird happens to the planets. As we looked out the window, the two planets appear to be growing closer together, while our concept of time of 1 hour per 1 hour remains constant (diagram 8.1b).

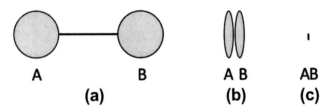

A   B   A B   AB

(a)   (b)   (c)

Diagram 8.1 ~ a) Human "at rest" on Earth perspective b) 99.99999% speed of light
c) 100% speed of light

In our example (8.1c), at 99.99999% the speed of light, we've reached the fastest speed the rocket ship can go. According to relativity, it is impossible for our rocket ship to go that little bit of extra speed to 100% the speed of light; it would take an infinite amount of energy to do it. So at this point, we need to switch our perspective from being in the rocket ship to that of being light itself. Let's take a light-centric perspective.

Using Einstein's equations, it is relatively easy to compute the time it will take light to travel from planet A to planet B. The answer is zero time. At light speed, the planets would compact so tightly together there would be zero distance to travel. We may have thought that since the planets were 100 thousand light years away, it would take light 100 thousand years to make the trip, but we would have been wrong. That is how long it would take light to traverse the space if we watched from Earth.

From light's perspective, it took zero time to get from A to B because planet A and planet B exist at the same place. The unique speed of light is so fast that it compacts the two planets into a single point in space. Where we perceive time moving at 1 hour per 1 hour, think of light perceiving time moving at zero per zero. From light's perspective, every moment is comprised of zero time and zero space.

Thank you, Mr. Einstein!

It is important to understand that zero time and zero space does not mean time and space do not exist; they do. In Chapter 7, we discussed additional dimensions and started out with the zeroth dimension where a point in space occupies zero dimensions. But don't flip back; diagram 8.2 will help us understand the concept. Here we have spatial lines that represent length, height and depth. Notice that at the point

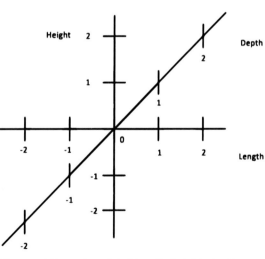

Diagram 8.2 ~ Axis point of length, height, depth = zero.

where all three meet, the value is zero. Space exists; it just happens to have zero value. If that intersection is represented by a point it would have zero value and be in the zeroth dimension. Once you have a continuum of points and make a line, that line would manifest in one dimension.

So let's take this one step further. Imagine another line representing time running through the intersection of length, height and depth. This junction of time would be zero as well. Because of Einstein's time dilation, we know that from light's perspective, a moment in time is exactly zero. A moment lasts for zero time and like the point, it takes up zero space. But we don't see zero-dimensional points, nor do one-dimensional lines naturally occur. Instead, everything manifests in four dimensions.

The good news is that all is not lost for you and me. There is a way to explain how we come into the picture. Remember that a continuum of points makes a one-dimensional line; a continuum of lines makes a two-dimensional plane; and a continuum of planes make a three-dimensional cube. In essence, our cube (three-dimensional universe) is comprised of lots of zero-dimensional points.

The problem with the cube is that, without time, it would be static. One cube would only represent one moment. We need a continuum of cubes, and that is accomplished by a continuum of points of time, allowing our three-dimensional cube (universe) to become an ongoing conglomeration of space. On their own, a moment of space and time, *spacetime*, occupies zero space and zero time. Collectively, the cube can become another cube, to become another cube, and so on.

Let's revisit planets A and B being so scrunched together they take up zero time and zero space. When we extrapolate the planets example to the entire universe. If planet A existed at the farthest distance possible from planet B it would still take zero time and zero space for light to get from one to the other. Even if we now include all the stars and planets in the entire universe, from light's perspective, the entire universe would get crunched together. Past, present and future would all blur together to the point where they all would take up zero space and zero time.

Looking back a few pages to the presentist and eternalist views of how the universe operates, we can now see how they are revealed depending if the universe is perceived from the perspective of objects with mass (presentist) or from light's zero-mass perspective (eternalist). People perceive reality from the presentist view; as *now* moments in time with a perception of things occurring in the past, and the anticipation of events occurring in the future. Because we don't move as fast as light, objects with mass see the world from this reality. Light, on the other hand, is able to perceive reality from the eternalist position; there are no past, present or future moments in time. They all exist as one collective moment. Neither viewpoint is right or wrong; they are both correct, and physics supports both views.

God Knows

Perhaps it's a good thing that we (objects with mass) don't move at the speed the light, but instead move at the slowest speed in the universe, allowing us to witness time going by moment by moment. The workings of the universe are complex, and I'm here to tell you that science has a lot of unanswered questions. How do we find the answers? Perhaps Sir William Henry Bragg, winner of the Nobel Prize for physics in 1915, said it best in a post award interview:

> *Sometimes people ask if religion and science are not opposed to one another. They are: in the same sense that the thumb and fingers are opposed to one another. It is an opposition by means of which anything can be grasped.*

In the spirit of Sir William, let's pool our opposing resources of science and religion, and grasp some of these tough questions regarding the universe.

Obviously, the Bible claims that time and space exist. After all, there are stories about kings, lands rich in natural resources, seasons and harvests. But the Bible goes to places where most books don't go—further than Harry Potter, Lord of the Rings, even Twilight. Where other authors write about unseen realms, vampires and witchcraft, they don't claim that their stories are based on truth.

The Bible does.

The Bible speaks of unseen heavenly realms, of angels and demons. It speaks of a loving God who created the universe and who is actively involved with creation and yet eternal.

We've already listed, in preceding chapters, Biblical references regarding heavenly realms, angels and God being actively involved with creation. Now we will focus on passages that address the light-centric issue of zero time.

To connect God with light's eternalist outlook we need go no further than revisiting the idea of God as being light. We've listed numerous examples in earlier chapters but here are a few passages describing God and Christ as light;

> As the appearance of the rainbow in the clouds on a rainy day, so was the appearance of the surrounding radiance. Such was the appearance of the likeness of the glory of the LORD. And when I saw it, I fell on my face and heard a voice speaking.
>
> *Ezekiel 1:28*

> Then Jesus again spoke to them, saying, "I am the Light of the world; he who follows Me will not walk in the darkness, but will have the Light of life,"
>
> *John 8:12*

> For just like the lightning, when it flashes out of one part under heaven, shines to the other part under heaven, so will the Son of Man be in His day.
>
> *Luke 17:24*

If God is light, then it is possible that God perceives the universe from the perspective of light. As Einstein's theory of special relativity tells us, from light's perspective, the entire past and future events of the universe could all be comprised within one instant, allowing God access to future events. Therefore, science supports the idea that God is capable of knowing everything that has ever happened and will ever happen throughout time.

As we have learned throughout this study, science has found light to be one of the most unique aspects of the universe. And when it comes to time perception, light has the inimitable quality of traveling at the constant speed of light; to be actively engaging within time as the transitioning agent for wave function collapse; be the energy provider in quantum electrodynamics; and be the universal glue that holds matter together. Light is not restricted to encompassing all past and future time at one instant, it also has the ability to be actively involved in the now.

Since light also has the ability to act within *now* moments in time, God (light) is able to align with Biblical passages that depict God engaging with humanity, even to the point where God can be surprised at the actions of someone. As strange as it would appear, science answers the question about how God can be all knowing and yet be surprised by someone's actions. Light engages the universe from the speed of light where all time occurs in one instant, AND it engages the universe within every *now* moment throughout time. Likewise, God can experience the universe in both ways. Science knows of nothing in the universe besides light that can accomplish both of these tasks.

God is Eternal

So far we have been working within the finite limits of time. What does science have to say about eternity? There are many Biblical passages that describe the existence of eternity, and God and Christ as eternal as well. Here are a few:

> *Jesus Christ is the same yesterday and today and forever.*
>
> *Hebrews 13:8*

> *"I am the Alpha and the Omega," says the Lord God, "who is and who was and who is to come, the Almighty."*
>
> *Revelation 1:8*

> *Now to the King eternal, immortal, invisible, the only God, be honor and glory forever and ever. Amen.*
>
> *1 Timothy 1:17*

On the topic of eternity, I need to be careful how I handle this sensitive subject. There are a couple theological interpretations regarding what eternity and forever mean. Some interpret eternity and forever to mean time ongoing and never ending, while others believe it is an indefinite length but at some point ends.

In an effort to stay loyal to my commitment to avoid doctrinal interpretations, when referring to eternity or forever in the context of God, Christ, the Holy Spirit, or the heavenly realms, I'll leave the doctrinal ramifications to the theologians. This study is to identify how science aligns with the possibility of God as described in the Bible, so I will describe how both definitions can function. But we'll have to move back into our discussion on additional dimensions to accomplish this balance.

Extra dimensions are not only needed to discuss eternity, without them God may be limited to being light and no more than light. In other words, if the entire universe were encapsulated within only our three dimensions, plus the dimension of spacetime, then where else would we find evidence of God? No worries, for both the Bible and science claim that extra dimensions exist. Here are a few Biblical references describing other realms outside our normal world:

> *And he carried me away in the Spirit to a great and high mountain, and showed me the holy city, Jerusalem, coming down out of heaven from God,*

> *Revelation 21:10*

> *I know a man in Christ who fourteen years ago— whether in the body I do not know, or out of the body I do not know, God knows—such a man was caught up to the third heaven. And I know how such a man—whether in the body or apart from the body I do not know, God knows— was caught up into Paradise and heard inexpressible words, which a man is not permitted to speak.*

> *2 Corinthians 12:2-4*

> *Then I saw a great white throne and Him who sat upon it, from whose presence Earth and heaven fled away, and no place was found for them.*

> *Revelation 20:11*

> *Which He brought about in Christ, when He raised Him from the dead and seated Him at His right hand in the heavenly places, far above all rule and authority and power*

and dominion, and every name that is named, not only in
this age but also in the one to come.

Ephesians 1:20-21

And He was saying to them, "You are from below, I am
from above; you are of this world, I am not of this world."

John 8:23

Jesus answered, "My kingdom is not of this world. If
My kingdom were of this world, then My servants would be
fighting so that I would not be handed over to the Jews; but
as it is, My kingdom is not of this realm."

John 18:36

According to String theory, there must be as many as seven extra dimensions, in addition to the four dimensions—length, height, depth and spacetime—for total of at least 11 dimensions. Picture our four-dimensional universe. Einstein's Special Relativity says that when moving at the speed of light, there is zero time and zero space. All four dimensions are wrapped up together taking zero room. If Einstein's theory is correct where it says that light within the electromagnetic radiation spectrum embraces all of these four dimensions, then what occurs in the extra seven dimensions? Both science and the Bible claim that more is going on beyond what we can observe within our four dimensions. The Bible describes a heavenly realm with a kingdom, a throne and mountains that do not exist in our observable universe. Scientists have full knowledge that anything could exist within the laws of physics in these extra dimensions we can't reach.

At this point, science leaves the door open for discovery. Time, as we know it within our four dimensions, may not be present or may behave completely differently in additional dimensions. Time could be endless, or it could go on and for an unspecified ending. The imperative fact here is that science does not contradict the idea of eternity. Although physics doesn't have specific answers in this area at the moment, it supports both possibilities of *forever* as either being non-ending or continually existing without a known ending.

> *Eternity is a really long time, especially towards the*
> *end.*
>
> *Woody Allen*

Timelessness

For those who hold to the belief that God is outside of time and does not experience the limitations of time, science supports that notion as well. It is believed that the big bang occurred in a vacuum, meaning that prior to its inception, there was nothing—no space, no matter and no time. Time did not exist until the inception of our universe. Science does not know what caused the universe to begin or what existed prior to our universe's commencement. However, if time as we know it within our universe did not exist prior to the big bang, and if God, existing beyond our four dimensions, created the universe, science can support the belief that God can exist outside of time and exhibit timelessness.

It is fascinating that science can align with the Biblical accounts of God being outside of time and also dwelling in additional realms. To be clear, God is described as more than just light. He is described as existing completely outside of our four dimensions. However, the aspect of God that is light is actively existing within our four dimensions. Not only is God outside of time, God is within time. God can be associated with both the presentist and eternalist realities. It doesn't have to be as Augustine thought—either presentist or eternalist. God can be both surprised on the one hand and yet know everything on the other.

Free Will

In discussing God as all-knowing at every moment, even possibly knowing all future events, there are those who may determine that we don't have free will and that God predestines everything involved with our existence. These people would assume that God makes all the choices throughout all of history. They don't think we have any free will, and that we lack the ability to make individual choices. To them, if God chooses, we end up in heaven when we die. Everything is entirely up to God.

Here's is the problem with that approach. We can't get caught up thinking that God acts exclusively from the eternalist perspective, where all time occurs at one instance and therefore God already knows our actions.

Knowing every event throughout time does not mean that God *controls* every moment throughout time. We need to take into account the ample biblical evidence that God acts from the presentist perspective and is active as each and every moment throughout time unfolds. The toughest thing for us to do is think of how both perspectives can occur at the same time, because we can't traverse time and be in two places at the same time. It doesn't make sense to us. But the world of physics says the universe acts much differently than we ever thought possible and that these two phenomena can both occur at the same time.

Here is an illustration to explain both perspectives—how we have free will and yet God can know our every thought and action.

Picture yourself looking in a full-length mirror. Every live action you make has the exact action taking place in the mirror's reflection. Now imagine yourself playing a best-of-three game of rock, paper, scissors with a friend, with the game reflected in the mirror. Each of you is trying to outwit the other and be the first to win two rounds. As it turns out, the game only takes a minute because you win the first round with rock crushing scissors, and also the second round with paper covering rock. You win the game.

Now, in this scenario, the game was played at the same speed both live and in the reflection in the mirror. But what would happen if the mirror lagged behind, so instead of taking one minute to reflect back the live action, it took 10 minutes? Every action, comment and thought that took place during the live action is exactly what the mirror plays out, just at a slower rate of time. Every choice made live remains the same as in the mirror. You can't make a new decision in the mirror scenario that differentiates from the live decisions because the mirror is, in reality, live. The two are not different.

It would be great if people had the ability to experience life from both the live outlook and the lagging mirror standpoint, but we only have the capability to go through life from the mirror position. Light, on the other hand, has the unique ability to take both paths. Light witnessed the live game played out within one minute, and the lagging mirror reflection of 10 minutes.

Now let's speed things up. The speed of light is much faster than our mirror analogy, so the entire universe (live) only took an instant to occur, but the mirror is lagging behind, taking billions of years to reflect the live version of events.

Be aware, this mirror analogy is just a way to explain this conceptually—it is a way that it could be happening. However, I don't want you to think that science says we are necessarily acting out mirror images. What science does tell us is that through quantum electrodynamics (Chapter 3), light does interact live with every atom in our bodies at every moment in time. So if God is light, there is a way God does not know our thoughts and actions until they take place, allowing for God to be surprised by our free will. In addition, because our perception of reality lags behind when it actually takes place from light's perspective, God (light) has a way to observe all our actions and thoughts well before we do, giving God a way to have pre-knowledge.

Through discoveries like Einstein's Special Relativity and General Relativity theories, science is helping us understand how God can be personal and surprised with us, and yet know what we will say and do at every upcoming moment in our lives. We are not light (as God is) and therefore don't have the luxury of experiencing all of time in an instant. Only God as light has that ability. We still go through life making choices. We are experiencing life one present *now*-moment at a time. Right now, as you are reading this book IT IS affecting your life and worldview. Your thoughts ARE happening in the present. It is live and you are experiencing free will to make decisions.

Enjoy your free will.

Chapter 9

Making Sense Of It All

We've covered some of the most important phenomena occurring in the universe—not only in the far off reaches of space, but within your very body. To think that you are mostly comprised of just three of the fundamental particles of matter may be hard to fathom. Isn't it wild that these three particles very likely exist because of specific vibrating frequencies of energy? Of the infinite possibilities of frequencies in the universe, only three produce you. And you thought you were so complicated. (You are, actually. That is the wonder of it all.)

In addition, all sub-atomic particles exist in two possible states. They don't always exist as particles of matter that we can see, touch, hear and taste. Particles also exist in non-materialistic, non-local, probability wave functions. Please understand that you and I are made up of trillions upon trillions upon trillions (keep going...more trillions) of particles, meaning that some of the time, the particles of our bodies transition to the non-matter state. It is as if the particle vanishes, 'POOF!' and then reappears. When parts of us are in this non-localized, invisible, wave state, they can exist anywhere in universe.

Something in the universe has to collapse the invisible waves to visible particles, or nothing would exist as we know it. Scientists studying this issue have conducted thousands of experiments with the same result every time. Particles will remain in the wave state until they are acted upon by an external agent, causing them to collapse into localized particles. The only agent known to collapse waves to particles is light.

The universe would not exist without light—the energy of the electromagnetic radiation spectrum. When it comes to particles of matter, light is everywhere at all times. Light is what gives electrons in atoms an additional energy source. Light is what bonds the electrons of atoms together so that a building stands, the Earth stays together and your body resists the urge to fly apart into a trillion pieces like a pack of skittles in a hurricane. Light collapses wave-state particles into particle-state particles. Light lets us cook food, see colors and develop computer technology. Light is in everything, everywhere and time revolves around it.

Still, of all the things we know that exist, we actually detect little of the entire universe. When scientists and astrophysicists discuss the *universe*, they are usually referring to what is known as the *observable* universe. The observable universe is comprised of what technological devices have been able to gather/detect from space. Even so, these devices are limited to how much of the entire universe they can detect. At best, astrophysicists think they have detected a mere 0.4% (1/250th) of the entire universe, although it is probably a much smaller percentage.

Now consider the portion of the observable universe we actually can see with our eyes. We learned earlier that we can only see things within the very short frequency range of visible light, out of the entire electromagnetic radiation spectrum. Anything detected by science in the other light ranges, such as radio, microwave, infrared, ultraviolet, x-ray and gamma frequencies, will not be detectable with our eyes. Only a minute fraction of the observable, particle-state universe contains visible light waves that allow us to see it.

On top of all this, we have to factor in dark energy and dark matter, which is outside the observable universe. Over 95% of the entire universe consists of dark matter and dark energy. Scientists know that dark matter and dark energy are out there, but they don't know what they consist of. Even though astrophysicists estimate there are more than a 100 billion stars in the Milky Way galaxy alone, that makes up a sliver of reality. When you look out into the night sky and see the countless stars, you are seeing less than .0000000000000000000000000000000000000000000000000001% (1 million, trillion, trillion, trillion, trillion, trillionth) of the entire universe with your naked eye. Nearly the entire universe is invisible to our eyes. We live in "illusions of reality" because we put so much credence in the tiny portion we actually see. Don't get me wrong, what we see is real. However, if you think that is all there is, you are terribly mistaken. And this doesn't even take into account what exists in additional dimensions.

According to string physics (specifically M-theory), things like photons (light particles), electrons and gravitons are not restricted to our three-dimensional universe. Through meticulous calculations, science now understands that seven additional dimensions must exist in addition to the four dimensions of width, height, depth and spacetime. In other words, our four-dimensional universe is part and parcel with the whole 11 dimension universe. We are the fish in the fishbowl staring out wistfully and wondering what lies beyond the living room. The laws of physics within our observable universe don't necessarily apply in these other dimensions. Beyond our reality, anything is possible.

When considering the existence of the universe and God, we have to take into account *all* reality, including the things we can't see, touch, hear or taste. The fact that humans actually know so very little of what is going on in the universe, I find it curious that people can be so bold as to proclaim that God or Intelligent Design CAN'T exist.

Future

On the one hand, quantum and string physics are uncovering the secrets of the universe, making possible incredible advances in such areas as health, technology and space exploration. On the other hand, science is creating more questions than answers. Science doesn't know how or why all these phenomena do what they do. In the search for solutions, scientists are spending billions of dollars and working extremely hard trying to figure things out. Diverse countries of the world have joined forces because the quest is too great to go alone. No other force on Earth is uniting countries and intellectual talent for the good of man like science.

The future for science is incredibly exciting. The discoveries in quantum physics of the past 100 years are nothing compared to where science can take us. Certainly, quantum mechanics have given us computers, satellites, cell phones and X-ray and MRI machines. However, the next two centuries will make today's technology seem archaic, even barbaric. (*You mean doctors actually had to cut into the bodies of their patients in order to preform medical procedures? Unbelievable!*)

Imagine having a cell phone in 1863 and being able to facetime with someone. No one could imagine such a device. A hundred and fifty years ago, the old-fashioned telephone didn't even exist, with or without a cord. Human flight was the dream of fanatics. War was fought with cannons, swords and horses. Antibiotics didn't exist, and advanced medical procedures included amputation—without anesthesia!

In 2006, NASA launched the unmanned New Horizons mission en route to Pluto that is today traveling at an impressive 36,000 miles per hour. At that speed, it takes 39 days to reach Mars and a whopping 78,000 years to reach Alpha Centauri—our closet star. (It's actually 3 stars closely orbiting each other). To give you an idea of how far technology has come in 10 short years, the University of Santa Barbara in California has been awarded a grant to develop technology that is expected to whisk a wafer-like craft the size of an iPhone through space at around 180,000,000 miles per hour. That's 25% of the speed of light. Instead of reaching Mars in 39 days, they anticipate speeding past Mars in a mere 8-10 minutes, with the lofty goal of reaching Alpha Centauri in just 18 years. But they are not the only ones. There is another group, called *Breakthrough Starshot*, that is also working on deep space travel. How will they do it? They plan on using the momentum of light waves.

Here are some scientific predictions for the next 200 years:

- People will live to over 200 years of age

- We will be able to efficiently harness 100% of Earth's energy

- Advanced humans will be cyborgs, having their minds and bodies augmented by technology

- People will teleport (de-materialize then re-materialize) from one city to another

- Humans will regularly travel beyond our solar system

It will be fascinating to see what 200 years of ingenuity brings. I won't see it. Neither will you. But if you are reading this book aloud to your newborn baby, she just might get a glimpse of it.

At the forefront of all innovations and inventions will be the use of light frequencies and nuclear forces in ways that are barely imaginable today.

New Information

There is power in gaining new information. The human race thrives on it. We know so much more now than even 150 years ago. Over the existence of our species, one hundred and fifty years is an extremely short time span, yet we are on an amazing information-growth trajectory.

There was once a time when most of civilization did not believe life existed on other planets. However, with new scientific understanding, life on other planets is plausible. Given the plethora of information, it is difficult to make a strong case that life cannot exist on other planets. Just because science has not found actual life forms on other planets and provided undeniable proof, doesn't mean that life forms can't or don't exist elsewhere. Now, there is nothing wrong with an individual believing that life doesn't exists on other planets. However, with all the new information gathered about outer space, it just doesn't make sense that anyone could distinctly make an argument that life *cannot* exist on other planets. Note the vast difference between *cannot* and *could*.

It is interesting that quantum physics has been around for over 100 years and yet very few people know much about it. Of course, it has developed over those years, and the amount of new insights has been enormous. And its distant cousin, string physics, is but a babe within the scientific community. It has only been around since the mid 1970's. But people are hungry for more understanding of these topics. Bring up quantum physics at a social gathering and a crowd listens with rapt curiosity. Based on what technology has provided so far, people are sensing the brave new world awaiting those who master quantum and string physics.

In addition to better lives, scientific information also brings fresh perspectives to the subject of God—his existence and nature. To formulate or re-formulate their beliefs, people need to be acquainted with scientific information. And that is the position this study has taken regarding the possibility of a God who created the universe. The scientific evidence correlating biblical records is akin to the mass of evidence supporting life on other planets. Objectively, modern science clearly points to the possibility of a God who created the universe. As people understand the world of quantum and string physics, they will be better equipped to form a belief regarding the possibility of the existence of God.

Sometimes it takes the right circumstances for something to take off and establish itself. It reminds me of the story of the sandwich. (Or maybe I'm just hungry.) Meat has been around for millions of years and bread dates back some 30,000 years. And yet, it wasn't until the mid-1760's that placing meat between two slices of bread became a popularized undertaking. The story goes like this: John Montagu, the 4th Earl of Sandwich, an 18th century aristocrat, was obsessed with gambling and found that placing meat between two slices of bread allowed him to continue his gambling and not get the playing cards greasy. Other gamblers saw the benefit and began requesting, "I'll have what Sandwich is having." After almost 30,000 years of meat and bread, the sandwich has evolved as a mainstay of modern casual dining.

It is time for quantum and string physics to catch on with mainstream culture as well. With the likes of Brian Greene and Michio Kaku as spokespeople reaching the public with best-selling books and videos, people are beginning to eat it up.

To be clear, Brian Greene and most other scientists are neutral regarding the issue of God. It is their intention to pass along interesting information, and in so doing, capture people's imaginations. It is my intention to direct the astonishing fields of quantum and string physics into the discussions of God, miracles, angels and heavenly realms.

An area that gravely needs an influx of new information is the debates involving atheists, evolutionists, naturalists and creationists. Sadly, these jousting matches between opposing philosophies rarely incorporate the modern scientific phenomena covered by our study. Most debates continue to employ arguments that are hundreds, even thousands of years old. The issue is not that the arguments are wrong, but that the debates are pointless. Each side has refined their arguments to a razor's edge, believing themselves victors and their opponents shredded husks of ignorance. Tragically, the real losers in these shark-fests are those caught in the middle—the public who is seeking credible information upon which to base their opinions. In the end, they leave the debates no better than before, and sometimes worse: undecided, confused and disillusioned with all sides.

The marvels of quantum science, combined with diverse philosophies and worldviews, holds tremendous potential for new perspectives to emerge and people who are curious about these philosophies and worldviews, have new information with which to form better intelligent opinions. I believe it is time for creationists, atheists, evolutionists and naturalists to convey the awe of the universe uncovered by quantum and string physics.

The God Model Versus Science's Top Models

We have covered some of the most important quantum and string phenomena pertaining to the question, "Can God exist?" Neutral science does a good job of telling us what is happening in the universe, but it does not have conclusive explanations for *how* or *why* these phenomena work. The scientific community does offer many possibilities, but it cannot agree on a single position. At this time, with science bereft of conclusive answers, the possibility of God is as good or better an explanation than any scientific interpretations proposed by the scientific community.

Indeed, the God model is the most comprehensive interpretation for *how* and *why* the universe acts as it does, according to quantum and string physics. Match it against the leading models. Here they are:

The God Model

Through the use of vibration and energy, a supreme being (God) created the universe and everything in it, including the laws of physics. All energy and matter, including the four forces of nature, was brought into existence and sustained through specific vibrational frequencies. This correlates to God's word: his utterances, commands and general discourse. Through vibrational frequencies, which include gravity, God brings form to everything in the universe. God uses light (electromagnetism) as a direct means to:

- Be omnipresent—present at every point in space, at every moment in time

- Engage in transitioning certain non-localized waves into materialized particles

- Be omniscient—collecting and transferring knowledge between particles

- Hold matter together once it has formed

- Govern time

In addition, the God model claims there are other realms that exist outside the realm that we experience within the four dimensions of height, depth, width and spacetime.

God is a higher entity, existing both beyond and within the limitations of an 11-dimensional universe as well as within our four-dimensional world. The presence of God through vibrations and light is actively involved in these four dimensions on a moment by moment basis, acting within our known laws of physics. Although laws of physics are most probably different in additional dimensions, God does not violate the laws of physics in our four-dimensional realities. In other words, God does not manifest as some unknown substance outside what we know to exist. It would be similar to someone creating a computer program in PHP language and all the updates and directives are done within PHP. The God model states that God wrote the universe in a language and abides within the rules of that language.

With the essence of God being light, Einstein's Special Relativity reveals that this would enable God to have the sole ability to experience all of time at one moment in time. And yet, because light is actively engaged in every electron interaction in the universe, God is able to have a presence within the ongoing moments of our four-dimensional realm. God (as light) is able to be within time and outside of time.

Every quantum and string principle I've discussed aligns with the God model. It is the most comprehensive of all proposed models because it addresses:

- The observer effect of wave/particle duality

- The delayed choice quantum eraser effect

- How particles are formed, maintain their form and how only certain particles come into existence from infinite possibilities

- The existence of non-local realms and additional dimensions

- Maintaining a consistent means of manifesting within these four dimensions while having a means to exist outside these four dimensions

- Operating within and without the restrictions of time

In comparison, here are the top scientific models proposed for explaining the phenomena of quantum and string physics.

Copenhagen Interpretation

This was the first general interpretation posed addressing the observer effect on wave/particle duality and simply states that the interaction with the observer is what causes the wave collapse. This model does not attempt to explain who or what the "observer" is. According to the Copenhagen interpretation, while a particle is a wave function it lacks a definitive physical reality until a particle is collapsed by an observer, then it has a definitive physical presence. The act of measurement (observing) affects the system and prior to collapse quantum mechanics can only predict probabilities of certain physical systems. Actual physical systems are only known once a wave function is observed.

This model remains one of the leading interpretations and is taught in most introductory quantum physics classes. Of all the phenomena covered in this book it only addresses the observer effect with wave/particle duality.

There are numerous issues with this interpretation. It has been argued that it takes a classical physics view where the results of a wave collapse are caused by the large, macro world of the physical world, and the state of the particle while it is a wave probability is meaningless. There is no regard for the particle while it is in the non-local wave state.

In addition, since the Copenhagen interpretation claims that a physical system does not have a definitive property until it is collapsed to a particle, there is no way to determine how a physical system (i.e. you) consistently becomes that same physical system throughout time. In other words, since we only know the possible locations a particle will appear once it is collapsed, this model has no way of explaining how you can actually appear as a whole, intact you. There should only be a possibility that a whole you appears. This is a huge issue for this model to address. This can be further argued when this theory goes up against some of the basic principles of classical physics:

- Principle of conservation of Energy: energy within a closed system can be transformed into various forms but can never be lost, gained or destroyed.

- Principle of causality: with every event, every change within a system has a cause.

- Principle of determination: every future condition of a system is uniquely determined by a preceding condition.

If there is no way to determine the end result of even a single particle until it has collapsed from the wave state, then there is no way to determine that some of the basic principles of science, as listed, will result. For example, how can it be known that if you bounce a ball it will bounce, if you don't know for certain where all the wave functions will be when they collapse? The act of bouncing involves conservation of energy, the principle of causality and the principle of determination. This theory is non-deterministic and lacks causal connection. In addition, of all the phenomena discussed, this model only addresses the observer effect issue of wave function collapse.

Many-worlds Interpretation (MWI)

The many-worlds interpretation has gained popularity amongst some quantum physicists. This approach states there are a magnitude number of universes (possibly infinite), where every possible past and future reality exists as a universe for every possible outcome. Imagine a bathtub filled with bubbles and each bubble is an alternative possible universe occurring. Each and every upcoming possible event outcome splits into additional universe bubbles. Although your life would be happening in many universes, you only experience the continual outcomes of one universe. You can't jump from one universe to another. Many-worlds interpretation is a deterministic model since every possible outcome is determined by an additional universe.

In this model, you are currently in another universe happily married, unhappily married, single, in prison, a paraplegic, a star athlete, believe in God... every possible scenario. You just happen to be experiencing the reality you are in. If you aren't completely thrilled with what you are experiencing in your current universe, don't worry, you are doing fabulous in another universe. It is a mind boggling theory.

People can get confused and think that parallel universes are based on extra dimensions when they aren't. An important point to make here is that multiverses do not need extra dimensions to exist. The theory can stand alone on the principles of quantum mechanics. It doesn't mean multiverses can't exist within extra dimensions, but the theory is not dependent upon extra dimensions.

This model doesn't explain the observer effect for wave function collapse because wave function collapse doesn't exist in this interpretation. The belief is that wave function collapse is unnecessary and is one of the objections physicists have to MWI. If wave function collapse doesn't exist how are scientists able to perform wave function collapse experiments in a laboratory?

The MWI also has issues deriving the *Born rule* of quantum mechanics, which allows for calculating the probabilities of different outcomes and the likelihood of each becoming the actual outcome. The MWI comes up with different likelihoods than the Born Rule, and since the Born Rule is an extremely accurate calculation, the many-worlds model needs to address the discrepancies.

I'll point out one more major inconsistency MWI has to solve to satisfy its critics. It's called *the preferred basis problem*. MWI needs to explain how each splitting of a universe maintains it's well defined locations. How does a lake, rock, apple always stay consistent throughout the process? It's easy for MWI to describe an individual electron splitting into two possible existences, and then two more, and two more, etc., as it moves along in time, however, if this theory is extrapolated to larger objects such as a rock with trillions of atoms, the rock should get blurry and overlap. MWI has a big problem trying to explain how the world can be changing and evolving on the one hand but maintain a well-defined structure of every object on the other.

Like the Copenhagen interpretation, the MWI attempts to address their opposition to the observer effect and the wave/particle duality issue. It does not specifically address quantum electrodynamics, delayed choice quantum eraser effect, bonding of electrons, vibrating frequencies, additional dimensions or time.

According to this model God is not only a possibility but God would be proven to exist. Since there is nothing in science that proves God cannot or does not exist, and the many-worlds interpretation claims that every possible universe exists, then there are universes that must have God. In addition, if there are universes that have God, then there are a magnitude (possibly an infinite) number of universes with God.

String Theory (Superstring, Unification, M Theory, Theory of Everything)

There is a belief that all the fundamental particles in the universe are made from vibrating frequencies of energy, producing what is best described as tiny vibrating strings or rubber bands. Where quantum physics describes particles as though they were a hard substance (think of a billiard ball), string theory mathematics determines that particles are very flexible and move around more than a hard substance, resembling something more in the line of a rubber band. One specific frequency produces an electron, another frequency produces an up quark, etc.

String theory also claims that an additional 7 dimensions must exist on top of the 4 dimensions- width, height, depth and spacetime of our natural world. These extra dimensions are believed to exist both as tiny curled up dimensions so small humans can't detect them, and a large membrane dimension that encompasses our four-dimensional universe.

This is an extremely important theory because it is the only model that attempts to unify quantum mechanics and gravity. It is the great hope of physics. Without something unifying quantum mechanics and gravity, physics says that both can't exist. Since we know that both the quantum world and gravity do exist, then something has to bring both together into one all-encompassing theory.

The biggest problem with string theory is that it can't be proven experimentally, and it is likely that we will never be able to do experiments to prove strings actually exist. This in turn leads to the problem that the theory can never be proven to be wrong.

Mathematically, string theory works and that may be the best this theory will ever be able to accomplish. Although this eloquent theory is the only theory that accomplishes one of the biggest issues in science, unifying quantum mechanics and gravity, it may linger for centuries unable to meet the testable requirements of classical physics. Here we have a theory delving into physics beyond the abilities of classical physics, and yet is tied down by the testable limits of classical physics.

String theory aligns and supports the God model.

The de Broglie-Bohm Theory or Bohmian Mechanics Model (Pilot Wave Theory)

This model says that pilot waves, secondary waves accompanying wave functions, cause non-local wave collapse and determine the single reality that we experience in the local particle state. This interpretation does not specifically claim what or who acts as the pilot waves. The de Broglie-Bohm theory primarily addresses the observer effect of wave/ particle duality and the measurement problem. It does not associate itself with the string phenomena of frequencies and extra dimensions.

Critics of this model propose it is impossible on the grounds that pilot wave theory occur explicitly in the nonlocal state, which is in apparent conflict with Einstein's special relativity.

In addition, since the pilot waves cause a specific outcome for wave function collapse, this leaves open the possibility the pilot waves have the ability to choose the outcome. Be aware however, that the concept of pilot waves gets dangerously close to the concepts of God and the Holy Spirit (discussed in the Bible). This interpretation is limited to addressing wave/particle duality and wave function collapse.

Quantum Bayesianism Approach (Qbism)

This model shows an agent dependent-world; meaning that your reality of existence is caused by your personal beliefs in what will occur. You have the power to make your own world. This interpretation does not address how the collapse from the non-local wave to the localized particle occurs.

This model does not allow for the objective probabilities of quantum mechanics, such as, the formula that predicts the probability that an electron in the wave state, when collapsed, will have an X% chance to appear at point A, and a Y% chance to appear at point B, etc., for every possible point in the universe. Keep in mind that this formula has been proven to be one of the most accurate formulas in the history of science.

Qbism says that wave collapse is based on subjective probability where the collapse is a case-by-case, individual result from each observer (you or I) as we constantly update our beliefs. According to quantum Bayesianism, the idea of one single objective reality—a world where everyone perceives the same world—is an illusion.

This concept of subjective probability versus objective probability is where Qbism becomes an issue for most physicists. To simplify the objective probability concept, consider that a coin has a 50% probability each to land on heads or tails when tossed. Subjective probability claims that if the observer believes, for example, that the tossed coin will be heads, the result should be 100% heads. Of course, if subjective probability were to be true, Vegas would be out of business and I'd be a lot richer.

Qbism argues that stuff is not derived from the physical state, nor is stuff made up from our consciousness. This model is saying that stuff comes from somewhere other than these places.

Virtual Reality Model

This model claims that we all live in a virtual world much like a computer game. A program based on 0's and 1's has been written with options of reality to occur. We live our lives within program code here on Earth with the freedom to choose paths along a timeline called life.

The observer effect of wave/particle duality is described by this model as the CPU of the computer, hosting all the possible outcomes—the wave function. The collapse occurs when a player (the observer) chooses an outcome. Light can be represented as the electrical charge needed to power the computer; therefore, it is omnipresent, omniscient and holds everything together.

The concept of additional dimensions in string theory is congruent with this theory as well. If people existed within a computer program and were restricted to the dimensional abilities of the computer, then additional dimensions would have to exist for the programmer to exist. In other words, the programmer can't exist within the computer the programmer is programming, right?

Interestingly, this interpretation is compatible with some of the problems string physics has in considering additional dimensions with laws different than our own yet having no way to prove them. Take a computer game such as Grand Theft Auto, in which you assume an avatar identity within the game. From the perspective of that avatar, it is living within the program code laws of the game; that is its reality. It has no understanding that another world exists with completely different laws outside the realm of the game. Nor does the avatar understand what supports its own world. It has no idea of electrical circuits, computer processors and memory chips, let alone non-virtual oxygen, water and fire.

But now things get interesting. What if the programmer added a twist by building into the game the knowledge that a master creator (a.k.a. the programmer) exists in a world outside the restrictions of the game, giving the avatars the added option to seek out the master creator and learn that new world? The game would suddenly develop beyond the mundane options of stealing, killing and racing cars, into searching for something that is more rewarding.

The virtual reality model needs a programmer—an intelligent designer. It is impossible for a sophisticated software program to randomly appear on its own. Hypothetically, the programmer creates the virtual world from nothing, writes the code (laws) for how the virtual reality works, and adds greater complexity until finally creating the primary players—in our case, humans. I'm not saying we exist inside a computer program; I'm saying this model describes God.

Summing Models Up

All of these interpretations, are comprised of human logic disseminating scientific data. It is interesting that these hypotheses vary widely in trying to explain the universe from every conceivable angle. Science is actually telling us they don't know how the universe really works, so they are trying everything. That's fair. That's why we call it *exploration.*

The greater point of this discussion is this: None of the leading models disproves the possibility of God. In fact, most of them support God. Of all the interpretations given, the God model is the one based on a written interpretation prior to science capturing their data. This is a major distinction that differentiates it from all the others. It is one thing to develop a model based on scientific discoveries; it is quite another to have a model written thousands of years before science discovers the validating evidence. One could argue that it is coincidence. And coincidence would be plausible if the Bible was consistent with only one quantum phenomenon. However, the fact that the Bible aligns with every quantum and string phenomena goes beyond coincidence. What we see is the intersection of two vectors: the Bible and science.

Now we get to the crux of the matter, does science support the possibility of God? The unequivocal answer is, *Yes.* The advanced branches of physics are dependent upon possibilities, specifically the possibility that their hypotheses and conclusions exist. The mandates of experimental proof imposed by classical physics don't work in the world of possibilities. At best they can eliminate a possibility, but the only way to eliminate a possibility is to experimentally prove it *im*possible

Those opposing the existence of God can't rest their beliefs in classical physics, which demands truth be proven through experiment, and puts the onus on believers to experimentally prove God's existence. Otherwise, the possibility of life existing on other planets, and every prominent scientific interpretation I just listed, are in the same boat. Now, with an understanding of modern physics, the onus is on the opposition to prove that God *can't* exist. Until that is accomplished, God is alive and well. Science has unintentionally proven that atheism is dead.

What to Do With the New Information?

There are billions of people on this planet who believe in God, and yet there are billions who don't. Personally, I prefer to explain God through my experiences and believe it is the best way to communicate who Christ/ God is. God-loving people do a fantastic job at *experientially* sharing about God's supremeness and love. However, I think we can immensely improve the way we *logically* communicate that God exists.

Many people who classify themselves as atheists or agnostics came to their belief due to important inquiries that were answered unsatisfactorily. People gave them weak responses, leading them to a logical conclusion that either "God can't exist," or "I don't believe God exists." Let me illustrate this. Let's look at a few legitimate questions that regularly get asked by atheists and agnostics and how they commonly get answered by Christians:

1. Question: Explain how God can know my every thought and the thoughts of all 7 billion people on Earth at every moment?

   Answers:

   a) Because God is God!

   b) God's ways are beyond our comprehension.

   c) He's personal and intimate.

2. Question: If science says the universe began with the big bang 13.8 billion years ago, how do you explain God creating the universe in only 6 days, 10,000 years ago?

   Answers:

   a) The Bible says that 1 day is like 1,000 years.
      (There are a number of variations from this Biblical premise, including; the possibility that time is slowing down; and, it is a metaphor to mean that each day in Genesis actually represents millions of years).

   b) Genesis is a metaphor of God's creation. It didn't actually take six days, nor did it occur 6,000 or 10,000 years ago. God created the universe at the big bang.

c) Science is wrong. There's no way we just evolved from some blob!

d) I don't know. God's ways are beyond our comprehension.

3. Question: The Bible says that God knows everything before it even happens, and yet it says that God can be surprised and even change his mind. How can God know everything throughout time and yet be surprised when something happens?

Answers:

a) God created everything from nothing, including time. Therefore, God is outside of time. Timeless. Being outside of time allows God to know everything that has and will occur in time before it even happens.

b) Stories in the Bible describing God changing his mind or being surprised did not really happen. They are made up to make God feel more personable.

c) God is a personal God and is actively engaged with humans at every moment. You can pray to God and he will hear your prayers. There are many passages in the Bible that describe God as engaging with us to a point where we can even surprise him and get him to change his mind. God is beyond our comprehension but there must be a way he can know the future as well.

d) umm… next question.

4. Question: I've never seen God. I don't feel a presence of God. I've never touched or heard God. Can you provide me even one thread of tangible evidence that God exists?

Answers:

a) You have to believe in God. It involves a leap of faith to experience God with your senses

b) God's ways are beyond our comprehension. It's hard to prove it in our world

c) All the stories in the Bible: Genesis creation, Adam & Eve, the pillar of fire, the parting of the Red Sea, the burning bush, Moses before God on Mount Sinai, Jesus walking on water—are evidence that God exists

d) Look around you: How could all this beauty and complexity exist without God?

Admittedly, I have used some of these answers myself when talking about God. Maybe that is why I usually avoided discussing God—I wasn't comfortable with the answers I gave to people, even if they were the best I had at the time. People are hungry for fresh, scientifically supported answers to intelligent questions. We've begun the process. Science has discovered that the universe is not simple. It is odd, dynamic and filled with layers of dimensional realities. It is obvious the universe is pretty weird. Believing that we see all there is has become a shallow worldview.

With this in mind, let's take another look at these four questions, adding in some science to complement explanations about God. In other words, answering these question from The God model perspective.

1. Question: Explain how God can know my every thought and the thoughts of all 7 billion people on Earth at every moment?

   Answer:

   > Great question. It just so happens that science has proven that light is omnipresent, meaning it is everywhere at all times as it interacts with every atom in the universe. Your brain is filled with axons, dendrites and chemical synapse firings where your atoms and light are working together. Light is involved in every thought you have at every moment. There are many passages in the Bible that talk about God being light. God uses light to be actively involved in our world. The Bible says that God is light, and science says that light can know the thought of everyone in the world at every moment of time.

2. Question: If science says the universe began with the big bang 13.8 billion years ago, how do you explain God creating the universe in only 6 days, 10,000 years ago?

   Answer:

   > Glad you asked.
   >
   > It turns out that science says both events actually could have happened. Our reality—what you see, touch, hear and feel—actually exists in two realities. One is an invisible reality and one is a visible reality. In order for the visible reality to become a visible reality, it has to transition from the invisible reality.

It's weird, but science calls this phenomena the wave/particle duality and the observer effect. Check it out on the internet. It's like this: Picture being in a pitch black room where you can't see anything until someone or something turns on the light. You exist in the room but no one sees you until the light is turned on. Once it is on, you exist to our normal senses. In a similar way, light has been scientifically found to be able to make the invisible reality transition to the visible reality.

There are numerous references to God being light found in the Bible. Remarkably, Genesis describes precisely what needs to occur according to science experiments for the invisible reality to transition to a visible reality. Outside of science experiments, Genesis is the only known document in history to accurately address the wave/particle duality and the observer effect. This is amazing because the two specific things that science requires that would seem impossible for anyone to know, are written in a book thousands of years old.

1) God is described as light

2) God is the observer in the observer effect

There happens to be no controversy between the big bang and the Bible. Both occurred.

3. Question: The Bible says that God knows everything before it happens, and yet it also says that God can be surprised and even change his mind. How can God know everything throughout time and yet be surprised when something happens?

Answer:

Science has revealed that one of the most remarkable things in the universe is light. Einstein helped us to realize that nothing in the universe travels faster than the speed of light. From light's perspective, everything in the universe, from the beginning to the end, occurs at one instant. The Bible describes a vital part of God as light, and therefore only light (God) would have this ability to witness all of time within a moment of time.

Now, because you and I are made of matter, we move slower than light, perceiving the world going by at a pace of 1 hour per hour. But light has this uncanny ability to be actively engaged with our atoms, enabling God (as light) to choose to inhabit our time-governed world, moving through time with us, sharing in life's discoveries together.

4. Question: I've never seen God. I don't feel a presence of God. I've never touched or heard God. Can you provide me even one thread of tangible evidence that God exists?

Answers:

a) If you believe that what you observe with your senses is all that is real in the universe, it will be hard for me to convince you God exists. Unfortunately, if that is your belief, you will also have a hard time believing in science. The advanced fields of quantum and string physics know that other realities exist beyond our immediate senses. Science declares that things exist in unseen realms and in additional dimensions. In fact, there is more going on in these other realms than what you and I experience on Earth. That's science. Now let's think about the Bible. It has stories about unseen heavenly realms, angels and a God that created our universe. Science says these things that seem to defy our known laws could definitely be real beyond what we experience.

b) The Bible has many passages describing God being light. Therefore, an aspect of God is light. That might not mean much to you on the surface, but it turns out science has discovered that light is one of the most important requirements for the universe to exist. According to science, light is needed to:

1) Help atoms bond with other atoms so everything stays together

2) Give atoms a continual source of additional energy

3) Transition atoms from an invisible existence to a visible existence

4) Light governs time.

Science says the universe can't exist without light, and the Bible says that God is light. Knowing the importance of light, I think there is more depth to the Bible when it says things like, "nothing can separate us from the love of God," or "the light of Christ is in us." This connection between science and the Bible is beyond coincidence. It is real.

Granted, these questions would need some extrapolating when addressing someone who knows nothing about quantum or string physics. I'm merely giving the condensed message to illustrate how these and other important questions can be answered in depth when we include science.

Humans Have Been Typecast

The human race is improving its technological abilities at an impressive rate, but we need to keep things in perspective. Scientists like to ponder the concept of intelligence, and the best way to do that is to compare it to other levels of intelligence. In 1964, the Kardashev Scale was developed giving scientists a way to categorize levels of intelligent civilizations based on their ability to harness energy. This classification also applies to possible alien life.

In the Kardashev Scale, a Type I civilization has the ability to harness 100% of its home planet's available energy. For Earth, this would include energy captured from such resources as plant life, fossil fuels, oceans, hurricanes and solar from the sun. Dr. Michio Kaku, Professor of theoretical physics at City University of New York, predicts humans to reach Type I in about 100 to 200 years[1].

A Type II civilization would have the ability to harness 100% of energy available from their mother star. This goes far beyond capturing solar energy. For example, it would involve having the capability to somehow channel the nuclear fusion energy produced in the star. Kaku estimates that humans are still 1,000 to 5,000 years away from achieving this ability[1].

A Type III civilization, having exhausted their home star, would have the ability of interstellar travel and to amass the energy from stars outside their galaxy. With this level of technology, they would have means of communication far beyond our current means on Earth. Our present communication technology might be so archaic that Type III civilizations would have difficulty communicating with us. Don't expect humans to have this proficiency any time soon, as Kaku projects it will still take some 100,000 to 1,000,000 years to accomplish[1].

Professor Kaku has added a Type IV level to the scale, describing an advanced civilization having the aptitude to seize energy extragalactically, such as the energy from dark energy. Note that humans have not even found dark energy yet[1].

Humans, on this scale, currently rank as Type 0. With our incredible intelligence and advancements over the past 100 years, it is humbling to think that we are a bunch of zeros. If aliens exist and would ever visit Earth, they would certainly have to be at least a Type I level intelligence and more likely closer to Type II. Movies portray us miraculously overcoming insurmountable odds and repelling every alien attack. However, in reality we wouldn't stand much of a chance technology-wise.

Categorizing civilization intelligence allows us to put the universe into perspective and raise some important questions. Given that humans are zeros, if God exists, this supreme deity would conceivably be greater than Type IV, more likely an even higher category, may be a Type VIII.

Is it beyond comprehension that something with magnitudes of more intelligence could even exist? Scientists don't exclude the possibility. Is it inconceivable that this intelligence we call God communicates with us, albeit in what may be described as a spiritual communication? Ask yourself: Do you believe a bunch of zeros that say God doesn't exist, or believe that maybe...just maybe, there is more to the Bible than you ever thought possible because its source is a level VIII intelligence saying there is more to this universe? Jesus Christ is an excellent example of this. Jesus claimed he was not of this world. His life was spent communicating to humans about things that exist beyond our four-dimensional world. He ought to know; he created it.

[1]Parallel Worlds, Michio Kaku, First Anchor Books, New York 2006 pgs. 307-317

Conclusion

Somehow the incredible details of historical value written within the pages of the Bible have lost credibility with science while other historical evidences such as the ancient cave paintings of Lascaux in southwestern France, receive international acclaim. Not to take anything away from the importance of the Lascaux cave paintings—they add to science by portraying what the surrounding animal life and culture was like some 17,300 years ago—but I'm not sure why it seems to be given a greater value than the Bible. Would there be an impact if someone all of a sudden uncovered a cave that had ten-thousand year-old paintings illustrating a human looking up into the sky gazing upon a being with streams of light beams emanating from it?

At first look, the Bible could appear to be a book filled with rambling tales of human strife, misery, destruction, war and some mythical deity that struggles to conform a species he supposedly created. It could be nothing more than a Harry Potter novel. To others, however, it is the most marvelous book ever written, filled with truths beyond our comprehension, the greatest love story ever told. Can these two sides ever be able to come together?

I believe they can, and science is a language that can help accomplish this mighty task. Most people trust science, and when new information is brought to the table that brings depth and clarity to a complicated topic like God, I believe science can be a common ground for intelligent discussions. I hope I communicated this to you throughout our study.

> *Now this is not the end. It is not even the beginning of the end. But it is, perhaps, the end of the beginning.*
>
> *Winston Churchill*

> *I don't know the future. I didn't come here to tell you how this is going to end. I came here to tell you how it's going to begin. I'm going to hang up this phone, and then I'm going to show these people...a world where anything is possible. Where we go from there is a choice I leave to you.*
>
> *Neo, from <u>The Matrix</u>*

Index

Abbott, Edwin 111, 188

angel 121, 122, 190

anti-particle 50

Aristotle 29, 30, 32, 136, 189

Aspect, Alain 68, 73

Augustine 137, 156

big bang 11, 30, 31, 34, 35, 55-57, 61-63, 75, 88, 94, 132, 133, 138, 141, 142, 156, 175-178

Blatner, David 37, 38, 80, 100, 188

boson 50, 88

Bragg, Sir William 1, 151

Calabi-Yau space (manifold) 116, 117

classical physics 18, 21, 24, 25, 27, 34, 80, 88, 91, 92, 94, 99, 167, 168, 171, 174

Copenhagen Interpretation 14, 167, 168, 170

dark energy 56, 74, 160, 181

dark matter 56, 74, 160

de Broglie-Bohm model 171

double-slit experiment 50, 52, 53, 68

Einstein, Albert 13, 19, 26, 37, 79, 90, 103, 116, 138, 139, 144-150, 152, 155, 158, 166, 171, 178

electromagnetic radiation spectrum 39, 41, 43, 44, 46, 53, 65, 86, 87, 92, 155, 160

electromagnetism 12, 18, 26, 31, 38, 42, 43, 87, 88, 91, 92, 94, 103, 123, 139, 165

electrons 22-24, 32, 37, 40-43, 49-53, 55, 74, 76, 77, 87-92, 146, 160, 161, 170

Emoto, Masaru 68

entrainment 81, 82

entropy 138, 140-142, 144

eternalism 136, 138

Feynman, Richard 13

flatville 110-115, 119, 122-126, 128

flow of time (arrow of time) 132, 139

force carrier 50, 88

free will 156

fermion 50

fundamental particle 92

gamma light 39, 40, 43, 86, 160

Goswami, Amit 74, 189

graviton 50, 88, 90, 91

Greene, Brian 12, 13, 15, 69, 76, 117, 118, 164, 188, 189

Hubble, Edwin 29, 30, 73

infrared light 39, 40, 41, 43, 44, 70, 86, 160

Kaku, Michio 31, 117, 142, 164, 180, 181, 189

Kaluza, Theodor 103, 115, 116

Kaluza-Klein theory 116

Kardashev Scale 180

Krauss, Lawrence 31

Lemaitre, Georges 29, 30, 32

lepton 91

many-worlds interpretation 168

mechanical resonance 81, 82, 87

microwave 40, 41, 43, 44, 70, 72, 86, 160

M-theory 26, 104, 116, 161

NASA 6, 56, 146

neutron 23, 32, 42, 51

Newton, Sir Issac 13, 18, 19, 94, 139

nuclear force (strong, weak) 24, 42

nucleus 23, 24, 42, 55

Ochiai, Yoichi 70

omnipresence 7, 37, 78

omniscience 7, 67, 75, 78

photon 37, 38, 40, 41, 70, 76, 88, 92

pilot wave theory 171

Planck (length, second, tension) 31, 91, 132, 145

Plato 29, 30, 32, 79, 136

presentism 136-138

protons 23, 32, 42, 51, 73, 74

Qbism 172–194

Quantum Bayesianism approach 172

quantum electrodynamics (QED) 7, 37, 40

quantum physics 21, 188, 189

quarks 22, 23, 32, 50, 51, 53, 88-92, 146

radio waves (light) 39, 53

Schrodinger 52

second law of thermodynamics (entropy) 140, 141

singularity 31, 32, 141

spacetime 22, 144

special relativity 19, 138, 139, 148, 152, 171

string theory 9, 26, 89-91, 94, 155, 170, 171

superstring theory 26

Tesla, Nikola 66

theory of everything (TOE) 170

time dilation 147

time-reversal symmetry 138

type I, II, III, IV civilization 180

ultraviolet light 39-44, 160

uncertainty principle 52

unification theory 26

virtual reality model 172

visible light 39-44, 86, 87, 160

wave function 152, 159, 167-169, 171-173

wave/particle duality 13, 49, 52, 53, 56, 59, 167, 170-173, 178

Wheeler, John 67, 68, 69, 70, 73

x-ray light 39, 40, 43, 44, 86, 160

Bibliography

Abbott, Edwin. *Flatland a Romance of Many Dimensions.* Pr inceton. Princeton University Press. 1991

Al-Khalili, Jim and Johnjoe McFadden. *Life on the Edge: The Coming of Age of Quantum Biology.* Black Swan Edition. London. Transworld/ Penguin Random House, 2014. Print

Arntz, William, Chasse, Betsy and Vincente Mark. *What the bleep!? Down the Rabbit Hole.* Lord of the Wind Films LLC, 2006. DVD, www. whatthebleep.com

Behe, Michael, J. *Darwin's Black Box.* New York. Touchstone, 1998. Print

Blatner, David. *Spectrums: Our Mind Boggling Universe from Infinitesimal to Infinity.* New York. Bloomsbury USA, Paperback Edition, 2014. Print

Branley, Franklyn, M. *The Electromagnetic Spectrum: Key to the Universe.* Toronto. Fitzhenry & Whiteside ULTD, 1979. Print

Craig, William Lane. *Time and Eternity: Exploring God's Relationship to Time.* Wheaton. Crossway, 2001. Print

Carroll, Sean. *From Eternity to Here: The Quest for the Ultimate Time Theory.* London. Penguin Group, 2010. Print

Comings, Dave E. M.D. *Did Man Create God? Is Your Spiritual Brain at Peace with Your Thinking Brain?* Duarte. Hope Press, 2007, 2008. Print

Cumrun, Vafa; Greene, Brian; Turner, Michael; et al. *Fundamental Lessons from String Theory, Special Relativity, The Dark Side of the Universe,* et al. Worldscienceu.com. online

Davies, Paul. *God & the New Physics*. New York. Simon & Schuster, 1983. Print

Dijkgraaf, Robbert. *The Unreasonable Effectiveness of Quantum Physics in Modern Math*. Perimeter Institute for theoretical physics. Youtube. com/watch?v = 6oWLIVNI6VA. Online

Eberle, Harold R. *Church History Simply Stated*. Yakima. Worldcast Publishing, 2012. Print

Eberle, Harold R. *Father-Son Theology: Systematic Theology for the Twenty-First Century Believer and Beyond*. Yakima. Worldcast Publishing, 2015. Print

Evans, Matthew; Adams, Allan; Zwiebach; *quantum physics, physics*, et al. ocw.mit.edu. Online

Falcon, Andrea, review of: Coope, Ursula, *Time for Aristotle*. Notre Dame Philosophical Reviews, 2006.

Falk, Dan. *In Search of Time: The History, Physics and Philosophy of Time*. New York. Thomas Dunn Books, 2008. Print

Goswami, Amit PHD. *God is Not Dead: What Quantum Physics Tells Us About Our Origins and How We Should Live*. Charlottesville. Hampton Roads Publishing Co. 2012. Print

Greene, Brian. *The Elegant Universe: Superstrings, Hidden Dimensions, and the Quest for the Ultimate Theory*. New York. W.W. Norton and Co., 2003. Print

Greene, Brian. *The Fabric of the Cosmos: Space, Time, and the Texture of Reality*. New York. Vintage Books/Random House, 2004. Print

Greene, Brian. *The Hidden Reality: Parallel Universes and the Deep Laws of the Cosmos*. New York. Vintage Books/Random House, 2011. Print

Kaku, Michio. *Parallel Worlds: A Journey Through Creation, Higher Dimensions, and the Future of the Cosmos*. New York. Anchor Books, 2006. Print

Kraus, Lawrence and Kaku, Michio. *The Big Bang*. 2012. Online

Mason, Phil. *Quantum Glory: The Science of Heaven Invading Earth*. Maricopa. XP

McFadden, Johnjoe. *Quantum Evolution: How Physics' Weirdest Theory Explains Life's Biggest Mystery.* New York. HarperCollins, 2002. Print

Polkinghorne, John. *Quantum Physics and Theology: An Unexpected Kinship.* New Haven. Yale University Press, 2007. Print

Ross, Addy. *What is Life? How Chemistry Becomes Biology.* Oxford. University Press, 2012 Print

Solar systems and beyond; Earth; technology; et al. nasa.gov. online

Susskind, Leonard and George Hrabovsky. *The Theoretical Minimum: What You Need to Know to Start Doing Physics.* New York. Basic Books, 2014. Print

Tetlow, Jim. *A Question of Origins.* Eternal Productions, 2008. DVD, www.eternal-productions.org

Tipler, Frank. *The Physics of Christianity.* New York. Doubleday, 2007. Print

Tipler, Frank J. *The Physics of Immortality.* New York. Doubleday, 1994. Print

Zukav, Gary. *The Dancing Wu Li Masters: An Overview of the New Physics.* 2001. Print

About the Author

My wife Randi and I want to say, "thank you so much for purchasing *A Quantum Case for God.*" It was an investment of thousands of hours of research, hoping in the end, to make the bizarre world of physics relevant, simplified, interesting, and give God glory. I pray you have many meaningful revelations about God's existence and that your relationship with Christ becomes even more alive than what it was yesterday.

In 1 John, 1:4 it says, "These things we write, so that our joy may be made complete." It brought the disciples joy to write and tell of their accounts with Jesus and I can identify with the joy that John describes. I love talking about God's  relevance to His creation and I am thrilled for what lies ahead.

It would be a blessing to have you join us in the dialog. I welcome you to be an active participant on our website and social media outlets. Let us know your stories. Maybe you had a supernatural encounter with an angel, or a physical healing, or a life-changing revelation. Perhaps you gave this book to a friend or loved one and it had an impact in their life. My wife Randi and I would hate to think that we were on this journey alone.

We live in a sweet little town in the northern most part of Washington called Lynden. Our son Tyler and daughter Hanna are now adults allowing us the freedom to travel and bring our message to where it needs to go. Perhaps you would like to have us come to your church and have us share in person.

I wrote *A Quantum Case for God* in a non-confrontational way, so that it could be read by those who may not believe in God. If you have any loved ones that need to hear a new perspective on God, I hope you feel it in your heart to pass this book onto them. As you give, I encourage you to cover the giving with loving prayer.

May the Lord's face shine upon you and be gracious to you.

Blessings,

Dennis Zetting

For those who want more, please go to our website www. quantumcreation.net. There you will find additional information and other content, such as, my video series where I go even deeper.

Email us at: info@quantumcreationministries.com

Follow us on: Twitter: DennisZetting@eyeremember.com

Facebook: Dennis Zetting

CPSIA information can be obtained
at www.ICGtesting.com
Printed in the USA
FSOW01n1340250716
23013FS